MW00639020

Genuine Journey Life After The Fairytale Ends

by

Brittney Baker

Edited by Caroleen Smiley, YPRS Editorial Services

"For every voiceless woman attempting to find her voice again, until you do...I lend you mine."

~Brittney "Genuine Gemini" Baker

ISBN: 978-1-7339058-7-9 (Paperback)

To Raynell "Supa" Steward

Thank you for your silent efforts, astounding support, and soft, yet firm, push to excel. You believed in my work and trusted my abilities from the moment we connected. First Black woman who demanded to pay me for my gifts. I'll forever praise you and will never forget your loyalty. You had thousands of options, yet you chose me and kept my name in the pot, until it was permanent.

My dreams are bigger because of you and this personal, passionate, project is finally complete under the watchful eyes of your love. Please continue to rest in the power of your beautiful spirit. Thank you for changing my life, and continuing to change the lives of others, one cosmetic product at a time. No matter how far writing takes me, I will always be the Crayon Case Editor. I love you FOREVER, Favorite!

To Myleik Teele

You've elegantly shifted the narrative and perspectives of so many misdirected women. You are a depiction of real compassion, who provides tangible advice and heartfelt strategies to assist others. Your constant sacrifices and decisions to do the "hard" work, has allowed my journey to be full of illuminated progression, and powerful accelerated events.

The door you opened for me, granted me permission to live without limits and will never be forgotten. I am reminded daily that richness comes from uplifting others and helping to change a negative mindset into one of positivity.

Thank you for sharing your successes, and failures, with the world, so graciously. You will forever reign as my "Queen of Stunts," and I will always be in awe of your transformative spirit. I salute you daily. Thank You!

For Big Homie, Pretty Lady, Big Bro, Buddah Buddah, &
Chugga Girl

Thank you for choosing me! I couldn't imagine life without you,
all. My heartbeats walk this earth daily and call me Daughter,
Sister, and Auntie. My life has meaning because of each of you. I
love you all so deeply and will forever honor and cherish the
dynamic we share!

CONTENTS

Chapter 1 Missing

The number 7 is intended to represent luck, happiness, and completion. It meant the exact opposite for the Bakers in this moment. **Seven** days, 7 long days, full of uncertainty, pain, and undeniable numbness; strong as Novocain. Her family wasn't built for this form of heavy devastation. Admittedly, there was serious dysfunction, but this level of desolation was never in their cards. When they saw her last, everything seemed normal. She was full of sass, quick tongued, with a strong, vibrant, energy. Over time, something had changed. Even her smile was different. They all noticed but said nothing. The body can protect and mask several things, but our spirits will never lie on us. She'd become a master at hiding her brokenness.

With strength garnered from watching the family

matriarch, she kept being resilient and resourceful but was a silent sufferer. That gloomy evening in May removed her smile indefinitely and everyone else's as well. **Seven** days of the unknown. Not hearing her voice was excruciating. The agony increased by the second, consuming them. Fear controlled them. All they could do was pray for signs of life. Flyers of the self-proclaimed "Queen of Inglewood" was plastered all over the city, pleading for help finding her. Was this what her impact had boiled down to? Had the story she intended to use to heal others caused her to harm herself?

"Detectives said no foul play. Prints came back; just hers, not his." her father forcefully slurred through his inebriated speech. "They still have her phone?" her brother's calm voice interjected from the other end of the room. "Yes, last call was to me," her father answered, his voice laced with distress. Her brother rested his hand on her mother's shoulder. "Mom! You've got to say something; please, say *anything*." Her mother was flooded with confusion; so much so it crippled her. It was as if the life in her body was non-existent. She had no special touch to help deal with this moment. Her father was angry and in acute denial. Her brother felt so hopeless. All he'd ever wanted to do was protect his only sibling. Nothing made sense about this situation. No clues nor answers, just worry. Brittney was **MISSING!** Where was she?

That was the recurring dream I'd been having for 9 years. I was gone, untraceable, just vanished into thin air, leaving my family responsible for picking up the pieces. For years I did my best to analyze it. Why would someone with so many dreams and goals intentionally vanish? Then it hit me! Being missing represented how much of me was gone; how far removed I was from my true authentic self. Unresolved pain often has us running; running away as fast as we can to safety or what we *think* is safety. I guess I should take you all to the beginning. Meet Brittney

Chapter 2 Nutty Norfside
Inglewood Cosby's - 1985

The average cost for a home was $89, 500 dollars, Ronald Regan was sworn in as the 40th President of the United States, Coca Cola introduced a new innovative soda formula, and a classic movie, "The Color Purple" made its debut.

A young, and seemingly prepared couple welcomed their first, and only, daughter to a family of 3, giving their son his only sibling. It's been said, I brought pure delight and joy to our family. Even though my journey to get here was challenging and unpredictable. Mom, a vibrant, sassy, and devoted lover of life became completely enamored with me. She never wanted a daughter and had prayed for boys only. Her intention was to avoid the hassle of raising a girl into womanhood. Dad, a sophisticated, Southern charmer, was determined to be present and raise well-rounded children that could carry on his evolving legacy.

I grew up on the north side of Inglewood, California. In the 80's, Inglewood was a ball of chaos, but my parents had a definitive plan to shield us from it. As I grew older, I valued that protection and honored the choices they made. I do often wonder what life would look like had we been given more exposure. Our lifestyle was pretty extravagant during that time. We had everything children needed and more. Spoiled rotten! I recall not ever wanting for anything. The love was plentiful. Our parents showered us with attention, affection, and support. We avoided all the stereotypes of black families in Inglewood. They hustled and set a precedent for us I will always appreciate.

Having two parents in the home, active, supportive, and proud of their children, we often were compared to "The Cosby's" of the popular sitcom "The Cosby Show". Our home was the safe-haven and reigned supreme in fun, light, and love. Dad and Mom met on the job. Mom, originally from St. Louis, Missouri, moved to California chasing dreams and following love. Her boyfriend, at the time, had family in Los Angeles. He convinced her that moving to the west coast would be the best thing for their relationship. More opportunities and room for their love to flourish. Like most women in love, she trusted and held on to every word he said. She wanted the "big city" life and was happy to do it with her significant other. Shortly after the move was made, he got caught up in some legal trouble back home and was incarcerated. After his release, his lifestyle got the best of him and he passed away, suddenly, from a drug overdose.

This left my mom shattered, scared, and extremely devastated. Her pride wouldn't let her go back to St. Louis. She was determined to survive this tragedy. She barely knew anyone and was literally alone. Her late boyfriend's family were reluctant to help and offered her lackluster support until she found a job at Southwest Plating in the heart of South-Central Los Angeles.

Dad, originally from Jackson, Mississippi, had been in California since he was 18 years old. He knew everyone and prided himself on being a well-rounded man. Smart, funny, and witty; he was a good catch. Family was a huge priority for him. Proud to be a true "momma's boy", he had no children, yet, and plenty of women flocking to him. He avoided drama, worked, and nurtured everyone who would allow it.

Dad would see Mom at work and noticed the slow progression of her depression. They bonded but as co-workers first and then friends. She thought he was a nice guy, but her heart was still with her late ex. Without trying to pry, he found ways to show his interest in her, which she always ignored. One day, she thought she was alone and was having a moment in the breakroom . The tears

7

streamed down her face as she watched the clock as her shift came close to an end. She didn't want to go home. Her living situation wasn't the best and she was being severely mistreated. These evil people were constantly stealing her clothes, food, and overcharging her for the room she shared. Losing close to 20 pounds in 4 weeks, mentally she was a wreck. Dad intervened and asked her to talk to him. When she shared her situation, he didn't hesitate to help. He was living in Inglewood in his bachelor pad; a beautiful 2-bedroom apartment. The second bedroom was only for when family would visit. He offered Mom the room with no conditions. Of course, she was skeptical, but he reassured her he only wanted to help. Getting her out of the current situation was the immediate goal. Then she could save up for her own place. They agreed to a 90-day trial. Those 90 days turned into a year during which they became really good friends but not romantically involved. She viewed him as her knight in shining armor. Now, I'm sure Dad had his own intentions, but he never projected them onto Mom; just wanted to see her get back to a healthy place. Eventually, the chemistry blossomed, and they became "we". My brother was born shortly after that, and things were looking very promising.

Dad was married before, which left him with a bitter and biased perspective on the matter. Although Mom wanted to be super traditional, and get married, she knew "life was going to be what it was going to be," and never pressured Dad about it. They lived a fruitful and blissful life with their baby boy. He was their miracle baby. Junior, my brother, was born prematurely and gave them a huge scare. Mom had an amazing pregnancy, but the end got complicated. They almost lost him and that made them appreciate every milestone offered to them. Another child wasn't off the table, but they wanted to wait and enjoy their son more. Surprise, surprise, two years later I entered the world ready to stir s*** up.

9

Childhood trauma is often unidentified until present

day experiences forces it to be revealed. Every family

has secrets and struggles.

Turmoil began to play peek-a-boo a few years after my birth. Dad was overtaken by alcoholism and the severe drug epidemic taking the nation by storm. Our brains will never allow us to forget impactful memories, regardless of age. I was 6 years old when I walked in on my heartbroken mother: defeated, confused, and desperately needing relief. She was kneeled over an open, empty, safe; hands activated for prayer. Dad was on a binge and had taken almost everything. Rent was due, food was needed, and we had nothing. Unclear of the actual circumstances, I didn't understand the severity of his actions, just felt the pain of a desperate mother. Moments like this became all too common and eventually, numbing. There was an unspoken activation occurring in me at such a young age. While I didn't know how or when, I believed I could heal my dad of all his diseases.

Dad was my superhero, just without the glitz and glam. No way he was a monster, selfish and lacking empathy for the family he created. To help me cope, I created an alter ego for whenever he was under the influence and learned to separate the two. Mentally, it kept a space for the Dad I knew and loved. Douglas was not my dad. Douglas was an unwelcomed visitor, who with each departure, I hoped would never return. Our home had a beautiful bay window, with a clear view of our driveway. Friday was payday and I'd wait in front of that window praying Dad would pull up, praying we wouldn't have a visit from Douglas; all before adding a second digit to my age. There were times when my prayers failed, and we wouldn't see Dad for days.

Now I know what you are thinking, "no way a child was able to gather all this information and come to these conclusions alone." You are partially correct. Mom and I were best friends. Our connection was beyond this world, and I literally stayed under her every moment I could. Learning, observing, and absorbing it all. This definitely forced me to grow up fast and with a jaded view of life. It was hard being just a kid, when I wanted to fix all that was crumbling around me. Mom blames herself for that. With her family miles away, and only handful of friends, she inadvertently vented to the one person who was all too eager to listen. Plus, she wanted to prepare me for life's curveballs.

Close family and friends knew the battles we faced but they either turned a blind eye or were discreet when the topic came up in conversation. They loved the humiliation Douglas brought on our family. They laughed at Dad, not with him, and it bothered me to no end. It seemed no one cared if he got better. They just didn't want him to complicate their lives.

My Dad was still my role model. I wanted him to fight.

He kept a job and did his best while battling his urges. Binges for the Bakers were hard. Douglas would show up and Dad would go missing for 2-3 days at a time, without notice. During one of his dreadful binges, he suffered a major stroke, was robbed, and ended up admitted to a local hospital as "John Doe." God spared his life, miraculously. While we were accustomed to his weekends away, anything beyond that created immense fear and anxiety for us all. He fought for his life alone, until Mom was able to locate him. Imagining my superhero in some random, abandoned, building alone, broke my heart into a million pieces. Some stranger taking his possessions, with no regard for his life. He had a family, he had a home, yet in that moment, he was all alone. When we got to the hospital, the nurse made Mom aware of his specific request, "He doesn't want his children in the room." My heart shattered, again. *"Why wouldn't he want to see us?!"* Mom later explained that he didn't want us to see him like that. I guess he wanted us to always remember him as our superhero; in the event something terrible happened.

Paralyzed and unable to function normally, Dad began the long road to recovery. I was willing to do whatever it took to help get him back to normal. With the support of an awesome medical team, he kicked rehabilitation's butt; quickly learning to walk, talk, and eat properly, again. I attended as many physical therapy appointments as possible. The staff were awesome, and even let me help with strength training. Throwing balls back and forth and helping him with weights. I was excited to be by his side. I remember seeing the joy in his face every time he beat a record. I was his biggest cheerleader.

Dad continued to fight for his sobriety and took his rehabilitation seriously. Our new normal was progressive, but short lived. Unfortunately, he still struggled with alcoholism. Having a parent with an addiction can feel hopeless. You couldn't keep expectations high because when you did, disappointment led the scoreboard. My parents' marriage was taking a huge blow. Our family was not in a good spot and eventually separation occurred. My brother and I went from having our dad present, and actively involved in our lives, to park visits and motel sleepovers. It traumatized me to my core. In my heart I knew my parents were trying their best but, concurrently, the experience fogged my vision of marriage and parenting. This was toxic, unhealthy, and needed to change.

Silenced

Children of addicted parents often isolate and become

very fearful of authority. They develop imposter

syndrome early, and typically look to appease others

as a way of soothing the loneliness brewing inside.

Mom worked hard to keep things normal but overwhelmed herself in the process. She became the sole providing parent, almost overnight. I didn't understand the shift, and it hurt me trying to figure it out. *"Who was going to help Mom?"* Our family was divided and she had no support. Dad's family had a difficult time accepting his addiction and often neglected or avoided Mom's requests for help. In the midst of one of their separations, babysitting became an issue because Mom worked evenings.

At a tender age, life and the innocence it had left was snatched from me. The art of silence was forced upon me like communion at church. I was sexually abused while in the care of a babysitter. My offenders were not only familiar to me, but did not look like offenders at all. *"What does an offender even look like?"* Young ladies grow up being trained to look out for certain things and pay attention to a specific type of behavior. *"But what if they show none of those behaviors?"* Mom grilled me every opportunity she got. We spoke about hygiene and inappropriate behavior; you name it, we discussed it. All the boxes were checked. Yet it still didn't protect me from the unknown.

My assault was composed of young, hormone raging, males doing something wrong for the sake of exploration. I considered myself collateral damage for being at the wrong place at the wrong time. No warning shot could've prepared me for this. They felt comfortable enough with me to request to experiment on me, and when I declined, manipulated me into feeling sorry for them.

Manipulation is a learned behavior. Youth are
exposed to doing whatever it takes to get what they

want. Adults do this as well on a larger scale, but it

starts at a young age. When you are abused sexually,

you'll create a narrative in your mind that makes it

okay. Mentally, you blame yourself. "What did I say

to make this occur? Why didn't I protect myself?"

My offenders were full of energy and being mischievous as we all began our wind down for bed. I recalled overhearing a conversation about sex but didn't understand the concept fully and wasn't invested in learning more. What I did feel about sex was: it was nasty, disgusting, and a deplorable act. I wanted no parts of it. Late in the evening, when everyone was presumed to be asleep, I heard "shhh" and snickers which startled me. I quickly positioned myself only to see my offenders dead smack in my face.

One playfully grabbed my gown and explained what was about to happen. Not a request, he **told** me what I needed to do, for them. The other one stood nearby quietly observing, and seemingly looking for direction from him. By the time I gathered my thoughts, the first one had his pants down. I remember saying **"NO!"** loudly, and his hand going over my mouth. He told me he wasn't going to hurt me, and they only wanted to "try it out". I declined again, but he was powerful, and the scariest thing ever in that moment. As he lifted my nightgown, my underwear still on, he parted my legs quickly, moved them aside, and inserted himself in me. I struggled to get free, but his hand clasped my mouth and his knee pinned my other leg. I shifted and twisted my body, apparently making more noise than they expected. The second one, presumably the lookout, told him to stop. He'd heard a noise from outside, so they quickly vanished back to bed.

I laid there, trying to collect myself. As mature as I was for my age, I was still a kid - a little girl full of innocence and promise. *"Did my innocence get taken away from me just now? Was I nasty, disgusting, deplorable?"* I gazed out the window and caught a glimpse of the moonlight. It was a full moon. I despise full moons now. My mind wouldn't let me rest but I had no idea what to do. I was frozen. The entire situation made me freeze. *"Should I go tell the babysitter?"*

Suddenly, the second one appeared again. He quickly shushed me and asked if I was okay. Still on guard, I was a bit relieved that he didn't try to attack me. He then shared that it wasn't fair that he hadn't gotten a chance to try, and he wouldn't be as aggressive. If I didn't allow him to try, that would be mean. I was scared, but in no pain, and feared being attacked worse than before so regretfully, I obliged, and he attempted to insert himself like the other one had done earlier. I felt disgusting and immediately said **"stop!"** He did and went back to bed, and I forced myself to sleep.

When I woke up the next morning, I had to face them as if what happened hadn't. They secretly pleaded with me to never speak of it, or they would be in serious trouble. I didn't want them to get in trouble. I was not in pain and felt it was a mistake.

Traumatic situations will make you bury them fast and long. Sexual assault victims aren't afforded the luxury of time. These choices are made for them, and they are stuck with them for life. The shouda's, coulda's, woulda's go out the window. You learn to internalize and try your damndest to forget.

I never uttered a word about my experience…until now.

I grew up thinking my violation was my fault so my story wasn't worth being told. There was also the huge fear of sharing and not being believed. No way anyone would take my experience for the truth it offered. So, I buried the experience, far and deep. You couldn't tell me that this secret wasn't going with me to my grave.

Never get so lost in your own world of hurt that you can no longer advocate for yourself. It starts an unhealthy thought that you deserve bad things and

before you realize it's a trend.

My body was technically still "pure". The young boys did not fully penetrate me; still, they had definitely violated me. I've walked with that shame on me for years, creating a nasty self-image. *"Are you a whore now?"* I'd often ask myself. That experience taught me people don't have to look, speak, or behave a certain way to be offenders.

As I matured, I grew to feel badly for my offenders, and wondered what had made them target me. What was lacking in their lives that pushed them to the point of my violation? I pray I continue to heal and wish the same for them.

Our families remained friendly, so I saw them all the time and as I watched them develop, I wished they hadn't made that one misguided step. I can only hope that my experience stopped them from doing it to anyone else. These types of situations occur more often than we'd like to admit, and are life altering. *"God, protect your children!"*

After the violation, my views of myself became negative and egregious. No matter how hard I tried, I couldn't help but feel dismissed and valueless. I knew God had bigger plans for me; they were just unclear at that moment. So, I built my armor and forged ahead, not allowing myself to remember. I ignored the shame and normalized the empty feeling gnawing at my insides. The crippling fear of what this would do to my family if I spoke up led me down a dark, silent, road.

Young girls who've been assaulted: you are more than your experience. I refuse to call you a victim because you are worth more than that. Know that what happened to you is not, and will never be, your fault. Choices were made for you, and you deserved better. Shine bright in your truth, and share your story, when the time feels right to you. The healing can't start until you do

Signs & Syndromes

Life was becoming more and more challenging, but I had high hopes. With dreams of becoming the next "Cosby Kid" I set out on an acting venture. Acting helped me mask my pain. I could be whoever I wanted to be, whenever I wanted to, and everyone accepted me for that. I stopped caring about being accepted as Brittney, instead, I let the art of acting be my joy. I studied the craft and constantly worked on improving my skills.

My parents were back together, and things looked promising for my future. There was one issue though, I was overweight and never fully fit the bill for my age bracket. Food and I became best buddies. I had my share of healthy meals, but I was spoiled so if I ever insisted on two double cheeseburgers from McDonald's, there wasn't a question if I'd be getting it or not.

When I was born, I had several abnormalities that

doctors promised would go away as I grew. Undeveloped fingers, toes, short in statue, and two different colored eyes. Every doctor's visit, I was nervous. I felt my "secret" would be revealed. However, they always assured my parents that my health was fine, and they had nothing to worry about.

At 12 years old, Mom suspected something was wrong. "Your menstrual cycle hasn't started." The rites of passage as a woman happened for her at a young age so it alerted her to dig deeper. Another concern was my excessive bed wetting. My parents thought it would pass, but it didn't. We later found out it was all connected to my illness. I still have accidents to this day.

Test after test, hospital visit after hospital visit, and nothing. But, Mom was determined to find out what was going on with me. After fighting for months to have me seen by a specialist, I was diagnosed with Mosaic Turner Syndrome. Turner Syndrome (TS) is a condition that affects only females. It is the result of the X chromosomes (sex chromosomes) being partially or completely missing. Turner Syndrome can cause a variety of medical and developmental problems, including short height, failure of the ovaries to develop, learning disabilities, and heart defects. I was relieved to have a distinct diagnosis. The pressure of feeling "not normal" finally had a name. Ashamed of my body, ashamed of the impure vessel I had been gifted with, I was happy to know there was a scientific reason for this madness.

Still, the diagnosis put an intense amount of strain on my confidence. I've hidden my feet for most of my life; constantly wearing socks and never being self-assured enough to accept my birth defect. I also had zero breast tissue so while girls my age flourished in that area, I stayed stuck with a flat chest. The biggest blow was hearing that reproducing was not an option for me. When the doctor told my parents I'd never have children, they didn't accept it. Mom would always tell me, "Don't listen to them baby girl. God will change this." I was conflicted. I loved God but didn't understand why he would do this to me. I also didn't understand why my mom was telling me to ignore these professionals and their medical prognosis. *"They knew what they were talking about, right?"*

First step into a normal life was starting a unique treatment plan. I was prescribed growth hormone shots, pills, and antibiotics. It felt like I was taking every medication under the sun. I had to give myself injections, twice daily. It was painful and embarrassing. My blood had to be constantly drawn and tested for abnormalities. The entire process was horrible, but I knew how hard my parents had worked to find this solution, so I stayed the course. The needles and medication became the enemy. Some days I hoped I wouldn't wake up, to avoid having to face them. When I turned 13 years old, I got really sick. The combination of medications had started to exacerbate my heart murmur. If continued, I wouldn't make it. A difficult choice was made; I'd stop taking all the medications.

I knew the day we made the decision that I wasn't going to have a normal transition to adulthood but would have to work twice as hard to reach my goals. So, the quest to become a big-name actress continued. The politics of it all became a lot for us to handle. Always being overpromised and overlooked became the narrative. It stopped feeling good to act. I blamed TS for it all and continued to bond with food because it never hurt me.

Food made me happy, and I never wanted to part ways with it. I tried losing the weight, but the TS made that more difficult. My parents did their best to balance enabling me. When they saw that my spirit was down, they offered treats or lavish meals. Dad especially spoiled me in this area. He took me to every new, fancy, restaurant that opened. Regardless of the cost, those Bakers were going to feed me, and feed me well!

Add to the mix me wanting to become more active. Junior was awesome at sports. I envied his abilities and wished I could have them. Exercise was not something I wanted to do. Primarily because I knew it wouldn't change how I felt on the inside. No one saw the ugly view I had of myself, and I knew no amount of weight loss would change that. I had to find my inner beauty first and that was going to take some work. Admitting that out loud was hard. We are trained to think highly of ourselves - be confident and let no one tell you differently. I experienced the opposite.

Battling my self-esteem, I found solace in performing, even if it was alone. Sometimes the characters I portrayed had beautiful insides. Some of the characters I created on my own did as well, which let me know an appreciation of my authentic self was there, deep down inside. I started creating videos using all the latest electronics. We had the top-of-the-line camcorder, camera, and all the cool gadgets

29

to make and edit footage. I did it all in the comfort of my home. On any random Saturday, you could walk into the Baker's residence to find some type of elaborate set up and me doing the weather, talking about the latest song, or any other topic that came to mind. As I recorded it all, in my mind, I was leaving traces of my legacy to the children I knew I would never have. God was building my confidence bit by bit, and I was thankful he gave me that piece of heaven.

Turner Syndrome is not a death sentence. In fact, 30% of women living with Turner's live vibrant and full lives. While those affected are often categorized and placed in very specific boxes, I chose to defy the statistics and encourage others to do the same. Battling TS is a gift, at the end of the day. I learned to see through things that could be considered ugly and find the beauty in everything.

Chapter 3 Finding Sisterhood

Forever Friendships

Friendships are the foundation that set a very

impactful tone for many.

I never fully felt accepted or like I fit in most places, and I always dreamt of having a "best friend". Seeing so many of my peers bond with each other, while having nothing solid on my end, truly messed with my psyche.

At age 10, I was introduced to Clara. It was the best year of my life. Clara was beautiful, funny, and super charismatic. Her mother worked at the school I attended, and we were very close. I clung to her because she enjoyed my company and always made me feel wanted. She frequently talked about her daughter, and how she knew we would be great friends once she transferred to this school. She was right! Clara and I instantly connected and became best friends. She accepted me for me and never questioned my insecurities.

What I enjoyed most about our friendship was the freedom it offered. She had a captivating personality and a way that made me comfortable with not only myself, but with her. I became obsessed with her and latched on like an orphan recently adopted by an amazing family. Clara always included me and made me feel super special. When she mentioned having another best friend, it made me uncomfortable and sad. I was selfish and wanted this special bond to be between me and her only. Being territorial over people is something we learn over time, and it usually starts at an early age. I was very protective over her and developed an unspoken attitude towards anyone she brought into our circle. When I first met Narissa, I wasn't impressed.

Narissa was gorgeous, confident, and a powerful force.

Her presence demanded your attention, and she was unapologetic in everything she did. We weren't fond of each other, and it showed. When introduced as "my other best friend" she quickly corrected Clara. "You only have one best friend...that's me." Navigating this change was challenging. I wanted her to accept and approve of me, but realized it was going to take time. The more Clara forced us to be around each other, the lighter the burden felt. Clara was amazing at maintaining balance and I owe my ability to balance my life to her. She managed both our personalities perfectly and merged us together well.

Eventually, Narissa and I got over ourselves. We realized that we loved Clara and since she loved us both, we might as well try to get along. Narissa and I gradually discovered how much we had in common and started to enjoy being around each other more. Blossoming friendship can be one of the most magnificent things in the world, when done correctly.

As young women, we needed each other for the life lessons ahead. Regardless of how we are raised, friends will offer different perspectives and insight. The laughs, the tears, and the unforgettable memories were priceless. I was finally forming a sisterhood and was so thankful.

High school was approaching, and we were extremely excited and ready to conquer this new chapter in our lives. The preparation was a lot of fun. Junior was already at the high school and had become very well known. This added a bit of stress for me because most of my life I had lived in his shadow. Not with Clara and Narissa, there was a clear, even, playing field; I truly appreciated that.

Our first semester went great. Learning and developing our own identities was cool. The opposite sex was becoming more of a leading discussion, and it always made me want to run and hide. Narissa and I shared similarities here. We stayed away from that department as much as possible. Clara, however, was a free spirit, who explored and took risks often. Being her friend was like being on a never-ending adventure. We always had to expect the unexpected.

I met Winnie around this time also. She was an attractive and very popular girl in school. What was ironic is, she didn't really want to be in the spotlight. When we bonded, she liked that I treated her differently. I didn't care about her popularity, or who she knew, I just really enjoyed her as a person. We would be creative together and do the goofiest things. The pressure of being associated with her always weighed heavy on me, though. We were polar opposites - skin tone, body type, and personalities. Others didn't get our friendship and we would often be asked, by our separate group of friends, "Why are you friends with her?" I loved all my friends and was just happy that my social awkwardness hadn't prevented me from developing these awesome relationships.

Clara devastated us with some news, one afternoon after

school. "I'm moving you guys and switching schools." WHAT?! We were totally caught off guard and speechless at the thought of losing her. We had no choice in the matter and that hurt more. A few weeks before leaving, Clara and I were hanging out and she told me how much she wished we could go with her. Narissa already had to fight tooth and nail to get into our current high school so transferring was out of the question, even if it was just a city over.

I felt for Clara, and never wanted her to be alone, so I worked hard to convince my parents to let me go with her. She was my best friend, the *original* best friend, and I'd do anything for her. I hadn't been this happy in a while and I think my parents understood that. Being connected to my friends gave me a purpose they could not offer. So, they obliged, and I was able to transfer with Clara. They even let me stay with her for extended periods of time because the school was walking distance from her home. Narissa didn't take it well, she felt a little abandoned but had developed her own sense of security and governed herself accordingly.

Being from Inglewood, you, unfortunately, have a target on your back instantly; especially when treading in uncharted territories. I laugh about it now, but that side of town was not anything I was prepared for. We began hanging with the wrong crowd in Clara's building. The influence of this new crowd was strong and hanging out trumped education. I began to miss school and fell into a trap of dismay without even knowing it. Clara fell in love and was really focused on nurturing that relationship. At times, it felt like I was not a priority. Things got intense when another teenage girl in Clara's building thought I liked her boyfriend. He showed interest but I wasn't in any position to have a boyfriend. That self-awareness made me proud, but also caused me much pain and turmoil. These teenagers weren't just average girls either. They were gang affiliated and rougher and tougher than I could ever be.

One morning, I walked to school alone and was cornered by four of them. "You think you cute and better than us because you from Inglewood. We getting that a** after school." My heart almost jumped out of my chest. We had exchanged words in the building before, but I never thought it would come to this. Needless to say, being jumped wasn't something I was looking forward to have happen. I needed to protect myself and the only thing I could think to do was tell a teacher and pray for the best. That decision changed everything for me. From that day on, I basically was looked at as a snitch. They ran me out of there quick and I didn't look back. Back to Inglewood I went, where I belonged.

Narissa and I bonded even more when I returned. She was my other half. When you saw her, you saw me. Our families were connected as well, and we all loved each other. It felt good to be back in this setting, however, leaving Clara broke my heart.

A few months later we received a call from Clara requesting an urgent meeting. *What could be so urgent?* We hadn't seen her in a while but had chalked it up to life happening. *Was everything ok?* The anxiety of it all almost killed me as we waited for her to arrive. "Guys, I think I'm pregnant!" EXCUSE ME?!?! Pregnant?! No, this was not happening! We'd talked about this previously. We had many plans and dreams, and children weren't a part of them. She was covered up in an oversized sweatshirt. The moment she revealed herself, and let us see her stomach, I was devastated. I immediately started crying. She asked us to go with her to an appointment to confirm. Narissa held it together, but I was not there mentally. Once we got the confirmation, Narissa broke down more than I had. We were so hurt and angry as we watched the innocence of our youth leaving us. This was our sister. Her being pregnant changed everything!

After that, things happened so quickly that it was a blur. Before we knew it, our beautiful goddaughter, Desi, was born; healthy and happy. We were so in love with her! She was perfect and calm and forced us to slow down and appreciate the little things in life. Seeing her smile, giggle, and just grow was such an honor. I had three besties now. Desi didn't slow down our progress at all. She just became a part of it. Wherever we went, so did she. Having a little human life to look after was refreshing and something I needed in my life at the time. I took my role as godmother seriously and would go above and beyond for Desi at all cost.

Once we all graduated high school, it was go time. I put the pressure on them to make this adult life we wanted and talked about happen, fast. I searched for 3-bedroom apartments and developed savings plans for each of us. I was determined, but my aggressiveness was a bit much for them. Even though Clara had a child, she was still a young adult, figuring things out. Narissa entertained my insanity but would always tell me "slow down." My plan to be an adult was already in full swing. I leaped and didn't look back.

Still a late bloomer, nothing about the opposite sex was alluring to me. I mean, I had crushes here and there, but never really acted on any of them. Clara introduced us to a small group of males she knew through a mutual friend. Karlton and Nintendo were good people, always had great energy, and never made us feel uncomfortable. Karlton connected with Clara the most. They really had a strong bond. However, we all got along, and they became like brothers.

When they introduced the Dubois twins to us, things got really interesting. Jimmy and Jalen were lively, rambunctious, and really into the streets. Something about Jimmy caught my attention, and my sisters picked up on it. "You like him BB! We can see it every time he's around." I

41

did but restrained myself from telling the truth. After more and more encounters, and more obvious feelings, I finally had to be real with myself and them. "Ok, I do like him, but I don't think he likes me. They encouraged me to 'go for it', but I had no idea what that meant. Socially awkward me didn't stand a chance! I went back into my shell and repressed my feelings. *"How am I, 20 years old, scared to talk to a man?"* The weight of my inexperience made me doubt my value.

As developing queens, we have to do our part to remain focused on all the glory God has blessed us with inside.

What happened next, I never saw coming. Hanging out as a group was always fun and one day, we decided to go to the beach to relax and have a good time. Knowing Jimmy would be there, I pulled out the best outfit I could find; even went and purchased a few things. I was hoping to catch his attention. Of course, as many underage youths do, we wanted to drink, and be as irresponsible as possible. I was tipsy before we even made it to the beach and hadn't been paying too much attention to my surroundings. When we arrived at the beach, everyone scattered and I was left alone, trying to fight back tears. What caught my attention then was how Jimmy was ignoring me.

Karlton had approached me and started making light conversation when out the corner of my eye I saw Clara and Jimmy sharing a moment. I was furious and exploded. I wanted to leave immediately, and without explanation, which confused everyone. Speaking up and being honest is something everyone claims they do, but when put in situations, you never really know how you will handle it. A flood of emotions came over me, and I was unsure if I was jealous from the obvious rejection, or if I was hurt that Clara, who clearly knew my feelings for Jimmy, was breaking an unwritten sister code. *"Who'd come up with this stupid code, anyway?"*

We returned to Clara's home to sleep off the drunken night. I still didn't know how to broach the topic of my discomfort or even what to say. I knew, though, that moment wasn't a good time. Narissa and I were asleep on the couch when I woke up, suddenly. Remembering the events from earlier that evening, I figured I just needed to relax, and go back to sleep. Just as I was about to fall back to sleep, my eyes focused on where I had left my belongings. *"My keys! Where were my keys?!"* Back up, I was in sort of a panic especially when I noticed that the front door was ajar. This was unusual because we were all inside, at least that's what I thought. My car was parked dead smack in the front of the house, clearly visible from the front door. I noticed that the windows were foggy but thought *"morning dew."* I figured I had left the keys inside, so I went to check. As I approached, I noticed the dim light of the radio and dashboard. *"Someone was in there and not in the front seat!"* I flung open my back door, to see Jimmy and Clara. My mouth dropped to the floor and a flood of rage filled me. I couldn't think of anything else but to leave. I hot tailed it back to the house to wake Narissa. "We're leaving!" I demanded firmly. "What? BB, it's like 3a.m., go back to sleep." "No, let's go now!" I yelled, forcing her up and making her grab her things. By then, Clara had followed me inside. Embarrassed and ashamed, I had no idea how to explain how I was feeling. "BB, we were just talking, relax." Clara reassured me as I headed out the door. When I explained everything to Narissa, she demanded we all sit down and have a talk. She was confused but was determined to not let this destroy our sisterhood.

Clara was always a straight shooter which I appreciate about her. When I was being the clingy, weird friend, she would always be the first to tell me. My yearning to connect to her emotionally was sometimes over the top and she would call me on it every time. This was no different. She explained her logic firmly and refused to allow this to break us. My sister meant the world to me, and no man should be able to break our bond. While I was caught off guard, I had heard horror stories about situations like this. I didn't want to lose my sister. In essence, we were all still kids attempting to be adults. We were able to discuss it and did our best to move forward, but nothing was the same after that.

Fast forward to a few months later and Karlton began to show interest in me. He was a complete gentleman. He was kind-hearted and super sincere, but I couldn't take him out the friend zone, mentally. When he asked me out, he was nervous, but confident, and I saw how much courage it took. It was just us, outside my house. I knew something was up when I received a call from him shortly after leaving a hangout spot and he asked if he could swing by for a quick second. He started off joking as usual, but then got really serious and calm. I'll never forget his words: "You're one of the dopest and most beautiful women I know, and I'd be honored to date you." It warmed my heart to know how much he cared for me, but besides not being attracted to him, my lack of confidence and overall insecurity caused me to gracefully decline. His friendship was special to me, and he was a very unique soul that I wanted to see flourish. I just couldn't see us being romantic partners. Even if I forced it, I knew I would never be able to offer him all of me. He was my friend, but only that, my dear friend.

Ironically enough, later, Karlton was who I chose to take my virginity. Plot twist, right? I know. Our chaotic friend circle had a lot of layers. I wasn't the only virgin in the group, Narissa was also. We had the same views about sex but then things changed and when she decided she was ready to lose her virginity to Nintendo, I felt all the pressure. I didn't want her to go through that experience alone and wanted her to feel supported, even if I wasn't ready. So, we set it all up.

Karlton and I were to meet and discuss the plan. This was months after the awkward and painful rejection. When I picked him up, I quickly muttered, "So, we're going to have sex okay. Preferably this weekend." He chuckled, took a breath, paused, stared me deep in my eyes, and with the most affirmative voice I had ever heard from him, responded, "No. We aren't B. I'm not letting you do that." Shocked was an understatement. "You don't want to do that," he continued. "You are worth more than that and mean too much to me, I can't do it." I was awed by his firm stance and full of relief. He was right, I didn't want to; I knew I wasn't ready. But, I'd do anything for my sisters, even if it meant risking my own integrity. Karlton and I finished chatting, laughed off the narrowly avoided disaster, and went back to my sisters to report the great news. I felt good about, and empowered by, my choice and hoped they would be proud of me.

When I arrived, I discovered I was now the only virgin in our sisterhood. Back to feeling strange and awkward. Back to feeling isolated and unnormal. I was disappointed in Narissa, but also proud of her for being so self-aware. She was ready and I wasn't. Sex changes everything about women, and if you aren't solid in understanding your actions it will destroy you. Being transparent wasn't enough for our friendship anymore. We all had to be on the same page, and we weren't. The next phase rushed in like a tidal wave for us.

There were extreme changes happening in our circle and I couldn't keep up. Narissa became very distant, cold even, and treated me like a disgusting fly swarming her food. She just wanted me away from her. Spending time together was different, and I felt every bit of the shift. I blamed myself though. If I had just gone along with the plan, maybe I'd still have one of my sisters since Clara and

I were still healing and carefully nurturing our friendship. She was often caught in the middle of me and Narissa's beef, but did a good job at maintaining balance, as always. Her favorite line to me was, "You're too young to be this stressed. If you love her, let her do her thing, everything will work out."

I worked hard to not be judgmental and allow Narissa to be free. When she met Blue, I saw the train wreck approaching fast. Actually, we all met him on the same night. Typical evening in a club, attempting to be grown. Blue was the loudest in the building. He had lots of energy and caught everyone's attention. His confidence was strong and made me a bit inquisitive. After chatting with him, I couldn't help but notice his focus was solely on Narissa. Narissa's head was all over the place and she was extremely distracted and didn't notice. The club became a bit raunchy for her, so she went to get some air. Blue miraculously found her, and they became wrapped in conversation. I was impressed with his assertiveness. Maybe this was what Narissa needed. When I saw that they were still talking, I approached and insisted they exchange numbers. Outbursts like this was not uncommon for me. I did it all the time with others but could never advocate for myself. They had already exchanged numbers prior to my interruption, and I left them to enjoy the rest of the evening.

I'm not sure what vibe or energy I was giving off after that, but Clara seemed to pick up on it. I knew because of our recent situation, she would compare the two. I was prepared for it. She found Narissa and expressed how it was inconsiderate and insensitive for her to show interest in Blue, knowing he and I had been talking initially. "What are you talking about?! BB is the one who told me to get his number. How is she mad?" Narissa was very big on clarity, so she marched right over to me confirm. "You good?" "Yes. You good?" "Yes. Clara says you're upset about me talking to Blue and that I am wrong." "No, I'm not, but you know where that's stemming from." The conversation was short and sweet, and we moved on quickly.

That was the last time I recognized my sister. She fell in love with Blue and I was not in support of it. She became a completely different person and consistently dismissed me. For some reason, his spirit rubbed me wrong all the time. I begged and pleaded with her to listen to me, but I had no chance against his gravitational pull; my sister was gone. The calls came less and less and eventually were non-existent. This might be an unpopular opinion, but I wish I hadn't given up on her. I wish I was mature enough to be patient with her like Clara was being. Clara was our glue. She never chose a side and tried her best to make a reconciliation happen, but our pride wouldn't let us. I navigated life without my 3rd heartbeat, and it was devastating. Anger, bitterness, and envy resided in me. We stopped speaking, days turned to months, months turned into years. 12 years of silence and living without my sister was so hard. Sisterhood would never be the same. Everyone that came after that suffered one way or the other.

Chapter 4 HEATstroke

Trauma Bonding

"Heat is intended to work with you and against

you, simultaneously. Our quest is to figure out

the balance. ~Matshona Dhliwayo

Love will never announce itself. It just arrives and has its way with you. When Heat entered my life, the model and definition of love I had was tolerance, sacrifice, and suffering. I never associated love with joy and was not able to fully articulate the shift in my spirit. Heat was extremely handsome, mysterious, charming, subtle, and nothing like any other man I'd come across. His confidence spoke before he did. Without fully understanding, I met the love of my life at the tender age of 21 years old. Our journey began suddenly and randomly, and as I reflect on it now, it was full of purpose and intent.

I'd been living on my own since I was 17 years old because once high school ended, I had been so excited to be an adult. I had worked the corporate jobs plus a few side hustles, set myself up well financially, and was living the adult dream life. My home became the center of our social universe, and I loved every moment of it. My girls would come over and we'd have such an awesome time.

The only downside - I was single and silently yearning for companionship. Even having the experiences I'd had, my heart still desired to be accepted and wanted by the opposite sex. Men would either be really mean or have clear sexual motives, that I was not able to handle. Even as I was surrounded by great spirits and energy, I felt alone. Those moments of sadness and loneliness would quickly be buried under all my adult responsibilities. Diving deep into my work and education, it was easy to forget how much I wanted to be connected, romantically.

Over the years, I coped with my awkwardness by showering everyone around me with the finer things in life. My goal was to become everyone's safe haven. My apartments became neutral ground to reset, recharge, and be rewarded. No matter the financial strain it put on me, I would never pass up an opportunity to connect with my circle of loved ones. Having a house full of people over was not uncommon, and even as an introvert, I advocated for more company. "The more, the merry" became my philosophy.

One evening, Karlton called to find out what the group was doing. As usual, everyone was at my apartment just hanging out. "Yo B, can I slide through? Oh, is it ok if I bring my boy Heat with me?" he asked. There had been lots of drama lately in our circle of friends, but we were trying to get past it all. My heart was skeptical about adding anyone new to our group. I was exhausted and tired of fighting my emotions. "Sure, just make sure he behaves. I don't have time for no weird s*** tonight." Within the hour, Karlton and Heat entered my residence. The moment I saw Heat, my life was forever changed. His presence was strong, and he demanded attention without uttering a word. I saw something special in him.

The evening went on - lots of laughs, jokes, and curiosity. This was around the time T-Mobile had introduced the Sidekick, a mobile device ahead of its time. They were partnered with AOL and offered the ability to Instant Message (IM). For my generation, this was the most epic way of communication. Making myself comfortable and allowing room for all my guests, I positioned myself on my living room floor not too far from everyone. My Sidekick kept chiming with messages from Clara. She was observing my behavior and could tell my focus was on Heat, and Heat only. My Sidekick buzzed and beeped in all its glory again, and again, in mid-conversation. I kept ignoring it knowing she was being annoying and teasing me. When it buzzed again, I assumed I was receiving another message from Clara, I quickly grabbed the device to silence it and was shocked at what I saw, "Hey, thanks for letting me come by. We can talk here so you can stop trying to avoid talking to me publicly." Confused, and overwhelmed, I calmly closed the device and tried to avoid the biggest nervous smile from forming on my face.

During our group conversation, Heat must have grabbed my device when I wasn't paying attention, found my IM name, added himself, and then messaged me. I was impressed and scared at the same time. *"No way he was interested in me!"* My lack of confidence wouldn't allow me to believe I was worth his acknowledgement.

> *This happens frequently for young women going*
> *through pivotal changes in their life. They become*
> *used to rejection and never can truly step into their*
> *purpose or worth.*

The evening ended, but Heat and I were just getting

started. We started off really slowly, but that didn't last long. We went from a few IMs a day, to spending weekends together, to being inseparable. He was so full of wisdom and dedicated to leaving a strong, powerful, legacy. I was captivated by everything he stood for and all he aspired to do. When we conversed, Heat was always willing to listen and made me feel important and comfortable. His ability to listen was impeccable. He never forgot anything and was very good at providing feedback. Not just regular, run-of-the-mill, feedback either but the in-depth, thought provoking, type. He noticed subtle changes about me and acknowledged them every time. Whether it was a hairstyle change, different nail color, or even a new perfume, he would make sure to let me know he noticed.

He wasn't scared to be honest and called everything out, accordingly. There was no gray area with him. He encouraged me to be more authentic, more vocal, and continue to step into my power as a Queen. We were smitten with each other, and I'd do anything to stay around his energy. I was paralyzed by our developing love and was content with being stuck...as long as I was stuck with him. Our passion for each other grew, and I was for certain my non-existent search for a mate had ended. He was my person, and I was thankful God had aligned us so perfectly.

Trauma as a youth is quickly hidden with materialistic things. Trauma as an adult becomes suppressed emotions seldom discussed or visited. We will endure trauma and silence ourselves because that is what we are trained to do. My generation, (1985-1995), was told we didn't know anything about suffering. Our pain was irrelevant compared to those of the older generations, so we endured, silently.

As Heat and I grew, so did the uncovering of our traumas. Family dysfunction, abandonment, and trust issues; they all showed up. He was fascinated with my upbringing and how it affected my current views and decisions concerning friendships and loved ones. Heat's ability to tell a story and have you feel every emotion as if you were there was uncanny. Our pillow talks were different. I could stare at him for hours and just absorb his wisdom.

One evening, we were outside on my porch having one of our many chats, when he expressed some trouble he was facing with the law and the stress it was causing him. He had been acting differently the whole week, and I thought it was something I'd done. I was relieved and happy that he felt comfortable sharing this with me, but sad he was stressed. My instinct to save and rescue turned on full-fledged. "What do you need; what can I do?" I asked with urgency. "Come with me; just be there," he responded. Simple. Just show up. I could do that. That day I truly felt his loneliness. I knew that feeling all too well and needed him to know I would always be there for him. I vowed to always be his friend, no matter what.

While we had been spending a lot of time with each other, we did not officially say we were an item. My lack of self-worth made me not understand why that was important, so I didn't push the issue. I was just happy to be around, and experience getting to know, him. Sex was not occurring or even discussed.

I was 21 years old and a virgin. Not your average virgin either, but a very green and scared one. My early childhood experience caused me to associate sex with fear. I was happy there was no pressure, but also concerned why there wasn't. What I'd grown to understand about men is they're sexual beings and make it a priority to engage in the act, often. Heat didn't. He wouldn't even come into my bedroom for the first few months. If he came over, and decided to stay the night, he would sleep on the couch in the living room. It was the cutest, yet strangest thing, but I obliged him.

My mind went in several directions during this time.

"Was he not attracted to me? Did he have other women who satisfied him sexually, and I was only the mental refuel?" My heart would hurt thinking about him entertaining other women. I had no past, but he did, and never was ashamed to let me know that. His crack at love had happened early. As the late bloomer, I found myself being unsure of how to handle things.

My advice to any young person battling this same thing, is: "Be patient with yourself. Give yourself the freedom to write your own chapters and don't let society snatch your pen away from you."

I became very possessive of Heat and was determined to get to the bottom of his philosophy. Trauma kept showing up in subtle ways for both of us, but we continued to forge a bond I felt was unbreakable. There is no play book for love, especially first loves, and I was really out here winging it. It's a dangerous combination being in love and naive, but it happens.

My prayer for those who will tread these uncharted

territories is that they listen more to their own

intuition and pay attention to red flags when they

present themselves. When it feels strange, or

uncomfortable, you are not overreacting. How you

respond to it all will determine your journey.

Court day came and I was overwhelmed with emotions. He was silent for most of the drive and as we made our way to the facility, I couldn't help but wonder, *"why me? Why did he want me here, of all people?"* I pushed my thoughts to the back and focused on him, the drive, and remaining calm. That drive was painful, but a testament to what we were building. I had his back and he had mine. We would take these uncomfortable journeys together. Later that evening, we had an in-depth conversation about the day and life in general. "Thanks for being there today. Your support means the world to me." While we still had not made anything official, I was glad to know him, to be in his presence. "Hey, no matter what happens, I got you. From this day forward, you will always have a friend in me."

When Karlton introduced Heat and I that evening, I had no idea how hard and fast I would fall for him. To protect Karlton's heart, I begged Heat to keep our connection a secret. We didn't tell our other friends right away either, and when we were around them all, we pretended that we were not together. In hindsight, there really wasn't anything to tell them. We held no titles, even though our chemistry was undeniable. Still, this led to us hanging out privately. One day, Karlton called wanting to stop by. I was nervous that him stopping by, with Heat already there, would expose our blossoming love.

I did not want to hurt Karlton, so I asked Heat to hide. At first, he refused, "I'm a grown a** man. I'm not hiding from this n****. If he comes and sees me, we just need to tell him." My heart was so conflicted. *"Tell him what? We* *liked each other?"* I felt my stomach drop with every thought and breath. When Karlton arrived, Heat finally agreed to hide, after my persistent nudging.

My goddaughter was there and with her smart, witty, self, innocently said, "Heat is in there," and pointed towards my bedroom door. "Oh. My boy here?" Karlton responded confused, but unfazed. I needed a hospital! My blood pressure was sky high, and I felt faint. Heat revealed himself and with no hesitation, they left the apartment and held a conversation outside. Time stood still as I waited for them to return. To my surprise, when they returned, all was well. That evening ended with laughs and love and was a true testament to the power of truth. I thank Heat for that.

During our pillow talk that evening, I was curious as to what was said, and how the conversation went. "I told him the truth. Simple." Heat was unaware that Karlton had feelings for me and for sure didn't know about the disastrous plan to sleep with each other. All he knew was that he cared for me and his friend. He expressed that with the utmost sincerity and caution. Approximately one month after that, Karlton and I had a conversation to clear the air. Things weren't awkward, but they were different, and I wanted to make sure we were okay. "We good B. Just promise me you'll be careful." After that, he became our always welcomed third wheel, and never interfered with our love. In fact, he supported it.

I desired Heat more than I'd like to admit. While I hadn't shared my sexual assault experience with him, or anyone for that matter, he was aware that I was a virgin, but never treated me differently because of it. This newfound attraction had all of my hormones raging, and I was becoming bolder than I ever knew I could be. We paced ourselves with our lust and found creative ways to exchange passion, usually stopping before things got too intense. I started an inside joke for store runs. Whomever was going, the other would always say, "Ok, and don't forget the condoms," always returning with no condoms. This playful banter went on for months.

One evening, he headed to the store, and asked me what I wanted, "M&M's, a coke, and don't forget the condoms." Normally he'd laugh, tell me I was crazy and head out. This evening, while he still laughed, he gave me a different look. That five second exchange was full of power and promise. He smirked and headed for the store. It was late so I started winding down. The day had been a busy one, and I was looking forward to my mini meditation time before everyone showed up.

As I showered, my energy changed, and I reflected on all that had transpired over the last few months. I thought about how happy I was and even the losses I had endured. When I stepped out of the bathroom, I heard the rumblings of the crew. They were back, in full force. I immediately noticed that my bedroom door was closed which was strange because I had left it open. Entering the room, everything around me became out of focus, and my brain went into a trance that I couldn't shake off. The gold writing on the black box glimmered, as if it knew it was getting attention. Closing the bathroom door quickly behind me, I smiled the biggest smile, as I felt the redness forming on my face. *"Am I blushing?"* My large closet mirror doors gave me no option to ignore what I was experiencing. Condoms. A 12-pack box of condoms was strategically placed on my side of the bed. My inner self screamed. I locked the bedroom door and disrobed, staring intensely at myself in the mirror. Negative self-talk started immediately. *"He doesn't want you, it's only a joke; look how ugly you are."* That went on for about 10 minutes before my trance was interrupted by the jiggling of the doorknob. The energy inside my bedroom was already high, but I felt Heat's energy even through the closed door. After quickly getting dressed, I rushed over to the door and let him in.

His smirk was all the reassurance I needed. "Yea, thought you'd called my bluff huh? Not this time," he joked as he closed the door, but he didn't lock it. I noticed that subtle decision and let it sit with me for a moment. If his intention was to have sex, why wouldn't he secure the room it was going to take place in? There was a house full of people steps away which was odd, but also comforting. We continued to joke about the store run and then conducted our normal pillow talk.

Heat had never been affectionate, but he was full of passion. I felt it in every word he spoke. Deep inside, the thought of offering my body to anyone, sexually, was off the table. I never felt safe around men after my experience. I constantly feared being violated and never felt as if I was worth anyone's time. But, Heat made me feel safe. He was non-pressuring, humble, and super accepting of my insecurities. I felt seen, I felt supported, and I felt loved. One of the most valuable traits he showed me was empathy. It was getting later in the evening, and like normal, we allowed the light from my television to illuminate our melanin infused skin. A music video channel was playing, and we zoned out to the latest trending song. Gently rubbing his head as we conversed, I glanced over and noticed how different his skin felt and looked from mine. He was perfect to me, and I knew in that moment, it was time. Our connection was already strong, but what if it could become stronger? I silently prayed to myself, *"Protect me. Make this experience positive and enlightening."* "Go lock the door." It wasn't an uncommon request, but he must have heard something in my tone, because he stared hard and assessed me before moving.

We were in sync in my opinion, so I'm sure he understood all that was going on in my head. As he proceeded to lock the door, I felt the bruised, battered, Brittney depart. It was just me and him - my friend, my confidant, my soon to be lover. He let me lead. Everything was at my pace. For someone who had been violated before, having that sense of security and control was extremely important. He had no idea how much that meant to me.

I had heard horror, cheesy, and gory stories about losing one's virginity and I was a little scared to discover what story I'd have to tell. However, Heat was attentive, gentle, and conscientious. No question was off limits, and he truly was patient with me through all my nervousness. "Are you ok?" "Are you in pain?" Are you comfortable?" was all he asked of me. His touch was like butter on fresh toast. I wasn't a kisser, neither was he, but we exchanged tons of fiery kisses. Everything went very fast but felt like an eternity. He made my biggest transition to womanhood really easy. When it was over, I had to ask myself, *"Am I still a virgin?"*. My body didn't feel any differently. Mentally, I didn't feel different either. A ton of joy flooded through me and all the worry and fear leading up to this moment was gone. No shame, no guilt, no horror...all love.

My confidence was boosted, and I turned up the boldness a notch. The next intimate moment we exchanged, I was requesting to try new things, positions, etc. Heat graciously declined and told me how crazy I was. "Do you know how much pain you would be in after? Chill out speed racer, we got time." I didn't know you could continue to fall in love with someone over and over, but after we made love, I did, every day, with Heat. Nothing mattered when we were together. He made being Brittney easy to understand and easier to cope with. I had found my person and was thrilled about it all

Senseless Choices

Junior's girlfriend had recently given birth to my first niece, Skylar. Skylar was truly heaven sent; a magical spirit, connecting our family deeply. She was a love baby. The day she was born, I felt that sensation that twins describe when they feel each other's physical pain. Her parents hadn't notified anyone, but my instinct told me she was on the way. I was extremely close with her mother, Journey.

Journey was younger than me but was mature because of her life experiences. She was a free, and beautiful, spirit, who insisted that no matter what happened our bond would stay tight. I loved how she loved our family and how much she cared for my brother. Skylar became my full-time responsibility, and I enjoyed every moment with her. I was determined to be a viable resource to them for whatever they needed. My scope of the world was pretty limited, even as an adult. All I ever wanted to do was love and be loved. If that required sacrifices, I was down with it. Just getting comfortable with the shift my life had taken, I felt proud of the balance I was able to maintain.

When Clara and her mom shared their intentions on moving out of Inglewood, I thought nothing of it. As time went on, the discussions continued and a simple, "You should move too" was all it took to pique my interest. Moving out of Inglewood was far from my mind because I loved knowing my surroundings. Even the unknown felt familiar. Leaving that would definitely be a learning curve and financially it wasn't the best move either. Still, I thought, *"Why not?"*

Right before I was introduced to Heat, I was the youngest sales executive for a new media company. They installed programming into public transportation, and I was responsible for the, recently acquired, entire Los Angeles region. Money was there but knowledge was not.

I had obtained my Associates degree, yet still felt so unaccomplished. This new love inspired me to reach for any and every thing. So, I made a choice. We were going to move miles away from Inglewood and start a new life. Palmdale, California was amazingly beautiful. It was very quiet but with just enough noise to make it welcoming. After a few visits, the decision was made final. Excitement rushed through me and felt as comforting as my mother's Sunday breakfast.

I had family in Palmdale, so mentioning the relocation to my parents didn't affect them as much as I thought it would. Clara's boyfriend, Brown, had practically become a permanent resident in my apartment, so it wasn't a question he would join us, too. The house had 3 bedrooms, 3 1/2 baths, and a gorgeous yard. *"This was not happening, was it? Were we really about to do this?"* Moving day was exhausting, but fun, and we got it all done.

The plan was to move, and I would cover all expenses

for six months while everyone established themselves. We were all supposed to find jobs within that time frame.

Being immature or underdeveloped in thinking will

make certain plans seem black and white, when the

gray areas are there, strong and prominent.

The fun of being in a newly renovated home caused everyone to forget our original conversation, even me. We had no business experiencing this lifestyle at 22 years old. We were all living our best lives and I held it all on my back with no regrets. Then our fur children - two gorgeous pit bulls - were brought into the equation and we loved them like we birthed them. The backdrop of opulence was carefully crafted, and we were all in. The biggest mistake was not setting clear boundaries and expectations.

I knew the ins and outs of maintaining a household alone and was confident that my leadership would carry over to the others. Those first six months were amazing, but also painful in discovery. You get to learn a lot about a person's character when you live with them. Cooking, cleaning, overall hygiene, it was all out in the open. Being in my apartment was a different experience than having a large home. An unspoken beef formed between the couples. Who should be doing what? Why is this person not doing more? Opinions and views were heavy from all ends, and I rested dead smack in the middle. I cared for and valued everyone and couldn't fathom placing blame on anyone.

No one saw my true suffering, primarily because I chose to hide it. I suppressed the depression and feelings of loneliness and just coped with it all. I didn't consider how my housemates must have been feeling. I'm sure it was hard for them, being thrust into a lifestyle and not knowing how to contribute to it. As expenses grew so did my anxiety. I had no idea what to do. My parents were always there to support, but they also stood strong on this being my choice, so I needed to figure it out on my own.

On a monthly basis I was dishing out between $2,000-$3,000 dollars with no steady income or help. My savings was being attacked. Doing my best not to complain, I resorted back to my silent suffering, and kept my views and feelings out of the equation. The love and good energy were all I wanted. Speak up and it would shut down all the chatter and good times.

Shame becomes the muzzle, but you will get tired of losing the battle, so say something, and be heard. Brittney today, understands the importance and value for advocating for self. Speak up, be heard, and don't assume people understand your plight. My struggle with not having a voice for years really exposed itself during this time.

The tug of war only got more intense. Clara made valid points during our discussions. The red flags she begged me to pay attention to went over my head. My heart believed she wanted me to be happy, but saw the storm brewing close by. Heat's opinions were always spot on. He was a veteran. When you've lived as much life as he had, that type of discernment and wisdom is bound to release itself. My challenge became staying in love or saving my friendship. Narissa was on my heart heavy during this time. I understood how she had felt now but wasn't willing to accept or publicly admit it. I told myself I could win this. However, the animosity continued to build, and I knew one of the relationships I had worked so hard to maintain would suffer eventually.

The chain of events after that were evil, dark, and nasty. I asked Brown to leave, ruining the bond he and I created. This also angered Clara and tarnished our sisterhood tremendously. Things got so bad that we almost physically assaulted each other. My sister, my best friend, the mother of my very first godchild and I, were calling each other out our names, and ready to throw hands. It was insane! I loved Clara with everything I had but we didn't see each other from our original lenses anymore. *"What was happening; who was I becoming?"*

A few months passed and Heat and I tried to get acclimated to our situation. We managed and always had each other but my savings were coming to an end, and things were beginning to look really scary. It was also strange being in the home, just the two of us. You get accustomed to the noise and the vibrant energy of others. Real melancholy set in; I missed Brown and Clara. Chaos is funny that way.

Through the transition, Heat and I bonded even more. He really became my best friend. We loved our fur babies and each other. Our time alone in the house was short lived, however. My aunt, Mom's middle sister, frequently visited California to get away from the Midwest. Mom loved when TT came to town. Her baby sister was always a huge motivator and positive influence over her. When they were together, nothing was off limits. TT was very hands on as the queen of "do it yourself". So, any projects around the house that Mom needed done, she would tackle, not waiting for anyone or anything. She was a beast with a toolbelt, and I always admired her a lot.

Growing up, TT hated how spoiled I was, and whenever she had visited, she would be vocal about it. She wanted my upbringing to mimic theirs. Full of blood, sweat, and tears. Dad loved TT and always welcomed her, but after his stroke, they began to clash. Her mouth was slick, although she was honest, and had pure intentions. This was the "favorite," but she quickly made the s*** list with him.

When I got the call that Dad and TT had gotten into a bad argument and she was headed back to St. Louis, my heart sank. Mom was so happy to have family in California; her spirit was always higher. TT pushed her big sister more than anyone else could. Their bond was special, and I didn't want to see it broken. So, when it was suggested that she stay with me and Heat, I didn't think twice about it.

Heat had a lot of adjusting to do when it came to my family, but he always put his best foot forward. While he still couldn't wrap his mind around the way we operated, he never gave me resistance about who we were. I mean, talking to my parents 5-6 times a day was a bit excessive to him. He would often get annoyed hearing our house phone ring off the hook for trivial, but meaningful, chats with either my mom or my dad. Still, he always kept his cool. When I told him about my aunt, he was hesitant, but also understood what family meant to me. I felt lonely and was beginning to show it, so he agreed, and TT moved in. The plan was she would stay with us during the week then go to my parents on the weekends, to spend time with Mom.

Determined to be the glue to keep my aunt and Mom together, while giving Dad a break, I went into this transition full of optimism. Things got interesting right away. TT is a very dominant woman, and you could not ignore her power if you tried. I was intimidated by her and had been most of my life. Truth of the matter was, my lifestyle was not anything TT would approve of, and having her see it would expose all I'd been hiding. I was smoking, drinking, having sex before marriage, unemployed, and supporting a man, all things as a black woman you get judged for, even as an adult. My parents weren't idiots, they knew all I was trying to hide and had just turned a blind eye to it. Now that I think about it, Mom and I never had the official, "I'm having sex," talk. I never spoke a word about it, and she never asked. I preferred it that way.

TT came and literally strong armed me in my own home. I can laugh about it now, but it was mortifying while I was experiencing it. She didn't care for Heat and was very vocal about it, to me. "He doesn't deserve *my* niece," she would tell me privately. Heat was super respectful and patient throughout the whole process. He was always truly polite and kind and stayed out of her way as much as he could. We used to smoke inside the house, but as a compromise, he would go to the garage or his car. TT was a loner who loved working out and doing house projects, so she stayed out of our way as well, for the most part.

One day, she got upset because she had made an observation. I had artwork up around my home, but only a handful of photos. Heat and I had taken a lot of pictures on a vacation cruise, so I had some of them printed and framed. "Why aren't there any pictures of my sister around here?" she asked angrily in passing. "I see you and Heat, but none of your own mother. You only get one but there will be plenty of him. Fix that today!" She made a valid point, but her approach was unacceptable. More moments like that occurred which made me very uncomfortable.

Asking my TT to leave my home was probably one of the hardest choices I had to make, but I needed to set boundaries. Yes, she was my aunt, but she was in my home and didn't see it that way. She ultimately went back to my parents for a few months, before deciding to go back home to St. Louis.

Heat never really revealed much about his family. It was complicated and I respected his choices to keep his sanity about it all. Still, I never met his mother and that bothered me tremendously. When he told me he wanted me to meet his aunt Asia, I was shocked, but thankful.

Asia and Heat had a special connection, almost like mother and son. Meeting her was amazing! She was sophisticated, classy, and full of street smarts. She came to our home and instantly treated me like I was her family. No warming up, or trial period, we clicked the moment we met each other. I saw a lot of Heat in her and it all made sense. The things I expected to hear and see when I eventually had the chance to meet Heat's Mom, I got from Asia.

After Asia visited, we, of course, exchanged contact information and she started calling me more than her nephew. It was the cutest thing ever seeing Heat get semi-jealous about it. It really didn't bother him, but he would play along. The bond between me and Asia grew strong, quickly. She would give me advice on any and every thing I needed. I could talk to her about anything, and vice versa. She was older than me, but young enough that it felt like a big sister-little sister relationship. I grew to love Asia and was thankful for our connection. She lived in Little Rock, Arkansas and we got the chance to visit for a few days. It was very calming being there. Our trip was short, but we enjoyed all it had to offer.

My money had officially run out and we started to fall behind on the bills. Heat and I looked for work but had no luck. My stress level was the highest it had ever been.

Always fatigued and having no energy, I knew the weight of it all was taking a toll on me. I was checking my email one day, praying for a job lead or update, when an email from Sallie Mae popped up. "Get your private student loan for $25,000, today." School was far from my mind, but my spirit told me to open up the email. Reading the requirements, I felt confident I could get approved with a cosigner.

Mom trusted me with everything. When I was in school, because I was under 25, she needed to be added to all my school documentation, so I knew her social security number by heart. Desperation pierced me in the heart, and I started the application process. *"Wait… I'm not a student anymore, how is this going to work?"* I closed my email and decided to forget about it but all that night, it haunted me. We could really use the money. Things would be fine if I could just get one loan and pay it back.

A while back, I had started thinking about getting back

into acting because I knew what that money would be like. Aligning myself, I had taken headshots, shot a demo reel, and sought representation. The demo reel was done prior to my move so it was difficult to watch because Clara was a part of it. If I had any chance at making it, I needed to be available during the day, so I looked for night jobs. When Spring Hill Suites called me, I was grateful, but also skeptical because it was in the city. I would have to drive back and forth every day. Still, I prayed I could land it. As I awaited my interview, a young woman, currently employed there, caught my eye. Eaglette was unapologetically herself, no matter who she was around, even at work. She was full of energy and listening to music as she cleaned the dining area. I judged her harshly as I waited, watching her every move and thinking, *"she's not poised enough for me."*

The interview was a breeze, and I accepted the position, which ultimately started my career in hospitality. The pay was horrible, and definitely not what I was used to making, but it was something, and just the thing I needed to keep my sanity intact. Driving from Palmdale to Manhattan Beach everyday was rough, but manageable because there was no traffic. I did that consistently for a couple of months before I began to feel the toll it was taking on me. I needed and wanted to get a job closer to home. There were a few hotels in the Palmdale area that I researched and tried to get placed in, but no luck.

During this time, Eaglette and I became friends. I liked her and found a lot of similarities in our stories. Under that rough exterior, she was the most pleasant, kind-hearted, person you could encounter. Our friendship was work based, for the most part, because I lived so far away. She would always try to convince me to stay in the city and hang with her and her friends. My trauma in friendships caused me to deflect and not want any new friends, but she wouldn't let that happen. We held each other down at work as much as possible, and I really started to connect with her spiritually as well.

It was around that same time Purple called and said she was thinking of moving away from the East coast. She wanted to know if she could live with me in Los Angeles. Purple was like the baby sister I never had. We met during my time as a promoter and marketing analyst. I'm a huge Omari (Omarion - I don't call him by his stage name - haha) fan and worked with T.U.G (The Ultimate Group) back when they were a thing. Chile… that is a story within itself!

Purple was my baby. She had entered my life at one of the best times and we had become very close. Distance caused us to not see each other much, but I would take trips to the East Coast often. I spoiled her as much I could. We went on several trips, and I even flew her and her friends out to California and gave them a full West Coast experience. She was one of my best friends, and I loved her dearly. Hearing her in need, I didn't second guess wanting to be there for her.

With the new job, my mind told me that things would be okay, financially, soon. I also thought she was old enough to work, and would be able to find a job, eventually. All signs led to go, but the haunting of the loan still lingered. I gave her the go ahead but asked for a few weeks to get prepared for her arrival. When I told Heat, he was fine with it, but also expressed concern about our finances. I didn't reveal much about the finances until I didn't have any money left, so he was in the dark about a lot of my thoughts and potential decisions.

That evening, I went to work and decided to complete the application for the loan. The cap was $40,000 within a calendar year. "Congratulations! You've been approved for $12,000 dollars." Because this was a private loan, the check would be sent directly to me. Wow! Prayers answered! We were going to be okay. At the time, having that lump sum of money wasn't strange for me. I learned the art of saving from my mom. She trained me to always have at least 2 months of my overhead saved at any given time. While I bumped my head a few times, I figured out how to do that, eventually. When I was working corporate jobs, I had plenty of disposable income and splurged whenever I wanted to, but still had something saved. However, all my recent financial maneuvers had thrown my system out the door.

Getting this loan was a win to me. I didn't share the approval with my mom, and that hurt me, still does today. She didn't deserve to have me be dishonest and have her perfect credit ruined by my behavior. I buried all the emotions and told myself, I would fix it all…later. Got us all caught up on bills and did what I knew to do best…splurge, like a dummy. Oh, what an idiotic idea that was! We had our lifestyle back, at the expense of my mother's credit. I kept a couple thousand dollars in the bank because I feared we'd be back in the same financial hole soon. Still keeping everyone in the dark, I looked for other companies that offered the same type of loan. There were tons of them, and I was like a kid in a candy store. I knew my overall cap but was determined to keep a good cushion just in case. I waited a while, but already knew what my next move was going to be. I felt under the influence all the time. High off the adrenaline of it all. I knew it was wrong. I knew what I had done was bad, but I ignored that and continued to live my best life. The next go round happened a few weeks later, this time I got approved for $8,000 dollars. I gave Heat some of it to go on a shopping spree and didn't blink or think twice about it. He was really into fashion and needed new clothes. Everything was working out. I wasn't in school but had found a work around for that while applying. Again, the question popped up, *"who was I becoming?"*

For some reason, Winnie had been on my mind a lot

those days. I hadn't seen or spoken to her in years. We had fallen out in high school, and things never were the same. I missed her and her family. I randomly decided to stop by her last known residence.

I was shocked to find her still there and surprised to be welcomed with open arms. We quickly picked up where we left off. She was pregnant with her first child and blessed me abundantly when she asked me to be her baby's godmother. She didn't care about our past, just the present. We trusted each other, and I was so honored she valued me that much.

Winnie knew about my infertility struggles, and always begged me not to worry. "Girl, I'll give you some of my eggs, don't worry." While I had my experience with Clara and Desi, as well as Junior and Skylar, Winnie truly gave me the opportunity to parent without being a birth mother. She involved me in everything and always wished me "Happy Godmothers Day" on Mother's Day. When she had more children, they all became my godchildren, with no questions asked. I adore her for that. Those little humans love me, and I love them more than they will ever know.

What I love most about Winnie is through it all, she always stuck it out with me. We bumped heads all the time, so sometimes we needed breaks from each other, but she was always there. We've seen each other at all the different stages of life. When we reconnected, I had become so broken, I didn't know how to open up to her, or let her in. This caused some strain on our relationship. There were days I felt neglected and not important to her which caused me to develop a complex. I felt she treated me poorly, especially when we were among her friends. I wasn't everyone's cup of tea, and it showed.

When I brought up our issues, she blamed it on my secretive nature. "You don't talk to me. You don't tell me anything and won't allow me to be a friend to you." She was right. I didn't want to let anyone else in. I feared it all. I valued her, very much, but we had different perspectives when it came to friendship.

Through it all, she never kept her children from me. Even when we were not speaking, she would always make sure they showered me with love. I appreciate her so much for that because I needed them more than ever when I went through the dark periods.

The time had come for Purple to relocate. We developed a detailed plan and were ready to execute it. Having my baby in California was epic! She was full of life and brought me an abundance of joy. Her and Heat clicked instantly as well, and that warmed my heart. They played video games together and developed their own bond. I couldn't believe I was able to have such an impact on someone's life.

While she and Heat looked for work in Palmdale, I continued to work at SpringHill Suites. The drive was getting more intense, but I thugged it out as much as I could. I tried a few other options like catching a train down, but the times were always off from my schedule. I was desperate to work in Palmdale. Heat and Purple got calls to interview with a hotel in Palmdale, but I didn't. We all applied, and the one with the hotel experience, me, was overlooked. I strong armed my way into an interview, but it didn't work out for any of us and we were back to the drawing board.

Things started to get sticky, financially, again and I resorted to what I knew best - finding loans. I found another company and got approved for $20,000 dollars. This would max me out completely for the year, and I understood, this was it. Everything was great, until the check came. It was made out to me and the co-signer, my mom. No way could I call Mom and ask her to sign this $20,000 dollar check and not explain what I had been doing. Fear set in. *"What was I going to do?!"* I held on to the check while I tried to figure out a plan.

Queen Karma

Desperation is the stealer of all things. My life was full of desperate acts, desperate intentions, and desperate emotions. It took me under swiftly.

I made the decision to remove my mother's name from the check and cash it. Going to my normal bank was too risky. It was a credit union connected through Mom's job. While they'd never called her about my account, I knew what I was doing was wrong and couldn't take the chance of it getting back to her. I had to find a check cashing place, instead. After a few failed attempts, I finally found one that accepted and approved cashing the check. The relief of it actually working, was enough to sustain me for a lifetime. Money always makes things better, especially when you are struggling. We were still behind on the bills, but almost at the finish line of being caught up. More bills got paid and I had a little cushion to hold us down.

It was mid-afternoon, on a day that I was off from work and lounging around the house. My cell phone rang, and the number was not one I recognized. "Hi, may I speak with Brittney Baker please?" "This is she. How can I help you?" "Yes, my name is Rick. I'm the Store Manager for Nix Check Cashing." The lump in my throat formed quickly. Nix is where I had cashed the check. I was in trouble, big trouble!

"The check you cashed with us recently came back as fraudulent. It was issued to two people, but when you presented it only one name remained on it. You care to explain?" The tears began and I was at a loss for words. Stunned by the entire phone call, I had no idea what was ahead. After sitting silently for a moment, I mustered up the courage to tell the truth. "Sir, the other person's name on the check was my mother's, and she didn't know about it, so I removed her name." "You should be ashamed of yourself! You have until 5p.m. to have your mother call me, or I'm calling the authorities to have you arrested for check fraud."

I was going to go to jail if I didn't act quickly. It was 2p.m., and I knew he was serious. Heat heard it all and was stunned. I was shivering and crying and all I could do was say, "I'm sorry." Purple was also confused but did her best to console me although she had no idea what to do either.

It was over! Everything was crumbling!

So much loss was chipping away at me. I'd lost Narissa, Clara, my goddaughter, and Brown. I had jeopardized my relationship with my aunt, Heat and I were holding on by a string, and now, I was going to damage the bond between my mom and I.

Had I been honest, just spoken to Mom, and dealt with her potential judgement, things might have been different. As I dialed her, I knew life was going to be very different from that day forward. "I'm so disappointed in you, I can't even stomach the sound of your voice," Mom conveyed her emotions at my urgent and unfortunate news. I had to tell her everything, and still needed her help to avoid going to jail.

She called Rick and worked out an agreement. I had roughly $6,000 dollars left, but he needed the full amount to be paid back. They had kept about $1,000 dollars in fees and after speaking with my mom, he offered to put that towards the balance that was owed. We still had to come up with $13,000 dollars in a week. Mom and Dad only had about $3,000 saved, so the balance lingered over us. They were able to borrow $4,000 from family members. I could only imagine how those conversations went, "Hey our daughter has been committing student loan fraud and identity theft. We need to borrow some money to keep her out of jail." There isn't a word in the human vocabulary that can explain how low I felt!

On top of that, I was still responsible for Purple. She had

come out here for a better life, not be subjected to my criminal activities. It was all devastating and I was not coping well. Barely able to recognize myself, I tried to hold it together, but broke down daily. Heat was supportive but still shocked at the severity of it all.

Mom saw an ad on TV by CashCall. They were giving people loans of $10,000 dollars and up but with horrible terms. It was intended to help people who were behind on their mortgage. She applied and was approved. She used the money to pay off the balance owed to the check cashing place and pay back our family members.

Criminal. I was a *criminal!* Rick called me again after the debt was paid to remind me how blessed I was. "Your Mom could have and should have pressed charges against you. You are so lucky and blessed!" A stranger reminding me of the goodness that was my parents was mind blowing. I never wanted to inflict this type of pain or cause this much disappointment ever again!

We were still in hot water, and I knew I needed to get us out of this whole. I explained the rest of the student loan situation to Mom and vowed to pay back every red cent. She was optimistic and understanding, but still very hurt.

My Dad and brother didn't handle any of this well. Dad didn't speak to me for a minute and neither did Junior. While I was wasn't officially in jail, the contempt they held for me was seemingly worse. Junior was typically laid back and nonchalant, but he didn't play when it came to his mother. It didn't take much for me to feel his rage. He was disappointed in me, and it crushed me. Dad battled with understanding why, and how I had formulated such a negative plan. We used to talk every day, and to hear him tell Mom, "I don't want to talk to her," when I would call, was mortifying. I was drowning and could see no life raft in sight.

Things continued to get out of control, and losing our home was now on the table. We couldn't afford to stay there anymore, with just my income. The job market in Palmdale was terrible, and as hard as we all tried, nothing was working out. I tried looking for cheaper places, and even considered living in a motel just to buy time before the inevitable happened. It was even harder because we had dogs, but we tried. Even Purple was willing to try to get a loan in her name with a co-signer. She was willing to humbly ask for that, to save me. I knew she was uncomfortable, but she was still trying to help us.

After having discussions with my mom, who explained the repayment options on some of the loans and that she was open to getting another loan to help us get on our feet,, A mothers love is unmatched! I asked Heat to try to use his credit to get a loan. It was all on the table. It didn't feel good but at least everyone was aware. Heat did get approved but only for $2,300 dollars. We needed every penny we could get at this point, so we surely weren't turning down any money. We thought about staying in

Palmdale; using the money to go to a smaller place, but things just weren't aligning.

Through all the turmoil, Heat's affection and love would show up randomly. One day, we were alone in our home, and I had just finished crying privately in the closet. To keep myself busy, I started cleaning up. He would often go downstairs, drink, smoke, and listen to music, especially when he was stressed. As I swept the hallway, I heard him coming up the stairs, he was inebriated, so I thought he was just going to bed. "Come here." he sputtered. "What Heat? I'm trying to sweep." I snapped. "Ok, but just listen to this please." He pressed play on his phone and the melodic, soothing sounds of Donnay Hathaway's... "A Song For You", started.

"You taught me precious secrets

Of a true love withholding nothing

You came out in front when I was hiding

Now I'm so much better

And if my words don't come together

Listen to the melody

'Cause my love is in there hiding

I love you in a place

Where there's no space or time

I love you for my life

You're a friend of mine

And when my life is over

Remember when we were together

We were alone

And I was singing this song to you"

My heart melted, and the tears flowed. He was so special to me, and all I ever wanted was to know he felt the same about me. I loved him so deeply. When the song came to an end, he didn't have a speech, or some long expressive confession of his love, he simply said, "No matter what happens, always remember this." He was super cryptic most times, but his vulnerability in that moment allowed me to hear him loud and clear. I held on to that moment for as long as I could. Needless to say, to this day, I can't hear that song without crying.

We made the desperate decision to leave Palmdale, move back to Inglewood, and try to figure it all out. Dad started to come around; I guess Mom worked on him a bit. He came to help us move and I had to remove myself from his presence several times so the flow of tears wouldn't be seen. This was all horrible! My dreams were all gone. Everything was simply a memory now. Did my best to keep it together but it was so hard.

The transition was painful. Heat went to live with his mom, while Purple, our dogs, and I moved into my parents' home. Heat and I still connected as much as possible. He would come over and spend time with me before I had to go to work. It was a foggy, thick, cloud of confusion but we tried to hold each other down.

Purple had caught a bad cold and was feeling terrible. She was my baby, and I always treated her as such but during this time, I didn't have it in me to be the nurturer. It was my day off and Heat had decided to stay the night with me. My parents were super traditional, and didn't play, so Heat and I slept in the living room on an air mattress. Around 2a.m., Purple woke me up, wanting her friend, and began complaining about her cold. The stress of what had transpired had taken a toll on her as well. This wasn't what she signed up for or what she was expecting. A part of me knew she wanted to go back to where she was most comfortable. I made that choice easier for her. The tension from all I was facing boiled over and I attacked her, verbally. "You're being a baby! I can't do this right now; you need to go home."

The next day we had a very tough conversation where I explained how I felt. It was almost like we were in sync because she had already called home and asked them to purchase a plane ticket. She was uncomfortable, unsure, and not prepared for life away from her family. It was hard telling my best friend she should leave, especially because she had nothing to do with any of the mess. She was an innocent bystander caught in the whirlpool of my drama. She wanted to salvage our friendship and the last thing she said before her departure was, "Don't let this change us Sis. I'm still your biggest cheerleader and you're still my favorite person. We are good, okay!" I knew she meant that. Her reassurance lifted my spirits more than she could have known.

When she got back home, she called me as she normally would and continued to sing my praises. "If anyone can clean this up, it's you. Fix it, Sis. You got this." Having someone younger, who looked up to me, be so strong, patient, and kind was powerful. Purple impacted my life a lot throughout the years, and I will never forget her kindness during my darkest time. Our relationship really could've went left, but she embraced me and all my flaws, and more importantly, so did her family. I had nothing but shame filled veins, but they never shaded me for any of it.

Heat and I were maintaining, but far from okay. One Saturday, he called me, as usual, to say hello. He was being sweet and sincere, saying all the nice things I wanted to hear. "I miss you, I miss your face, and I can't wait to see you." Suddenly, rage overpowered my ability to receive any of it. I felt faint and wanted to vomit. I quickly said bye, got off the phone, and tried to calm down. I didn't know where this strong disgust was coming from, but I was sick of him and my mind said, *"end this. He doesn't want you anymore anyway."* I think it was the feeling of being easily replaced that haunted me that morning.

Whatever came over me, took the lead. I paced my bedroom floor for maybe 20 minutes or so after we got off the phone and my heart was racing. I literally felt sick and knew a purge of some sort was trying to happen. I dialed him and let whatever had gotten a hold of me take over. "I don't want to do this anymore." I quickly uttered.

Confused, I could almost hear him collect his thoughts before responding, "Wait what happened? We were just good! I don't understand…" I started attacking him verbally, and he quickly shut down. He let me curse and demoralize him and said nothing. No screaming, no counter responses, not a word. When I was done, he made one statement, "There is no coming back from this. I hope you know that. Remember, you asked for this." Still angry, I was confident and proud of my decision, so I stood firm. We ended the call, and, yet again, my life was altered and full of fog. *"What did I just do?"* I loved him! He was literally the biggest joy in my life. *"How could I be so careless?"*

Whatever spirit had jumped in me left a few hours later. The reality of my words and actions began to set in. I called him again and surprisingly he answered, obviously not in the best mood. "Look, I was tripping. I didn't mean any of it. I still want us to work." I humbly expressed.

"Naw, I'm good. I told you - ain't no coming back from this." He calmly stated. Wow! It had literally only been a few hours. I had made a mistake and did what I thought was best for the both of us. He went on to say we could be "friends," but our relationship was done, per my request. I sat in a daze for a few hours. *"This wasn't my life! I would be waking up any moment now."* We didn't speak for the rest of the day. Over time, our "friend" calls and interaction became less and less. I was single again and it hurt like hell.

Heat became colder and colder, but still offered me a friendship. We had a few mutual connections and that made it hard for us to ignore each completely. I supported him in any way I could and was willing to do whatever it took to see him smile.

Young women will easily throw themselves away if given the chance. Do your best to understand your worth. We aren't pouring into ourselves enough and can easily knock ourselves down to nothing,

unnecessarily. Don't subject yourself to self-sabotage.

It's a disease that is hard to shake and will consume

your life. I wish I had spoken out more about what I

was feeling back then. I wish I hadn't assumed, and

relied only on jaded, one-sided, views. When you

allow yourself to create your own narrative in toxic

situations, you always miss the perspective of the

other person.

Around this time, I decided that instead of healing, I wanted to hurt. I guess it could be considered my "hoe phase". I wanted to be a hoe so badly. Seemed like the whole "good girl" act was a thing of the past. Besides, I wasn't a good girl anymore, anyway, right? Dad would greet me by saying, "What's up BCC (Blue Collar Criminal)?" At first it was an inside joke, but then it spread to family and friends, and everyone started calling me that. I had earned every bit of it.

So, a hoe I'd become. I was terrible at it! No one took me seriously. I tried going out, too awkward for that; tried blind dates, too scared for that; had a terrible failed attempt at a one-night stand - it was horrible. I tried everything to numb my pain. *"Why was this so hard?"* Hoeing wasn't for me, but I didn't want to accept that.

Still working at SpringHill, Eaglette and I got closer, especially since I was back in the city now. Her vibrant energy was just what I needed. She took me everywhere and I tried numbing my pain with fun, laughter, and plenty of liquor. I needed all of it at the time. She worked hard to help me see my beauty and told me often how special I was. I never believed her. All that I had done, everything I had become, it was all too much to take in, and I simply wanted to run. Eaglette would not let me run from her. She stayed on me and forced me to enjoy my life. She never complained when I constantly talked about Heat and the pain I was in. "You're young B. You'll find love again, forget him!"

I tried to take a page out of her book, tried to be carefree, but it didn't work. We were joined at the hip, Eaglette and I, and it was important to have her with me during this time. We experienced all the ups and downs of life together, and she always made sure I knew she would be right with me through it all. What was refreshing during that time was the lack of judgement from her. Never turned up her nose, never questioned my decisions, just always rocked with me. It's been said Black women can't have sisterhood without some source of envy or beef but based on the friendship I had with Eaglette, I would've argued you down because we literally had no issues. If I wanted to call Heat, she didn't discourage me. If I wanted to do something nice for him, she encouraged me, but always set a disclaimer, "Friend, I'm team you, regardless. Stuff can't get too out of hand though, because I'll spaz out, quick." She didn't play about me, and I didn't play about her.

Even through all the pain, I didn't blame Heat. I knew we were over. Asia always checked in on me to make sure I was keeping my head as clear as possible. She would say, "NieceyPooh, come live with me. You're done with Cali and I need your spirit out here. I'd laugh and tell her she was tripping. California was home. She called me out every time, "Girl, you only staying because you hope you and my nephew will reconcile. I'm not stupid." She was right, I was holding on for my family and for him. But, to be honest, I was ready to run.

I was finally introduced to Heat's aunt, India, due to an unfortunate incident. After a few phone calls, India and I developed a bond and, just like Asia, she began to take me under her wing and treat me like family. As our bond got closer, Heat casually let me know that it wasn't the best choice. "Look, I get it, you a little vulnerable right now, but that's not the type of friend you need in your life." Asia said the same, "Y'all have two different lifestyles NieceyPooh. stay away or stay aware." I ignored them both.

India wasn't a horrible person. In fact, she was everything I wanted to be at the time. Beautiful, inside and out, confident, career focused, and street smart.

Sometimes your admiration for people can distort your view of their character.

We hung out, I helped her, she helped me, and we always kept it super real with each other. She'd call and hear that I had been crying and say, "Nope, we not doing that today. I'm on my way." She talked to me with no filter, "You think my nephew crying over you right now? Hell no! He's with some b****, having the time of his life, while you trapped in the house crying. You not no p**** female, toughen the f*** up." All her rawness, all her aggressiveness, I absorbed, and allowed to help me push through the pain. I trusted and appreciated her.

When she asked me to help with some transactions, I didn't think twice about it. I wanted her to know I heard her, and I could be tough and street smart. All I needed to do was go into a pharmacy and pick up a prescription in my name. What was she going to do with it? I obviously knew I was dealing with controlled substances, so I had an inkling, but didn't do my homework to find out. She wasn't this huge kingpin or well-known drug dealer.

First go round, perfect; picked it up with no problem. That was easy. She continued to be an ally and supported me in ways I didn't even know I needed. She championed me, always reminding me of my intelligence and assuring me I would get through this break up in one piece. I loved her very much.

Heat's birthday rolled around and I wanted to do something nice for my "friend". I also wanted to remind him that I still loved and would always love him. I orchestrated a small get together in Hollywood and did my best to go all out. I even ordered a custom cake with all the things he loved on it. I noticed that evening he was more distant than usual. He didn't want to sit by me and barely wanted to talk to me; it was odd. Maybe he knew I was trying my hardest to win his heart back. I was failing miserably.

Asia came for the celebration and seeing her, and India together was amazing. They both noticed my low energy and gave me pep talks, individually. I made it through the evening but felt ostracized. Heat was clearly showing me he didn't want me anymore. I know the initial blow of the breakup is supposed to be the hardest, but the constant reminders of the dismantling were even more devastating. I put myself in these positions though, no one asked that of me.

A few months later, India told me she needed my help again. Same drill as the last time. She asked me to meet her at her house and she would take me to the pharmacy. The first pharmacy was a small Mom and Pop one, so when she told me we were going to Target, my stomach did a jig. They say your intuition always speaks before you do. I definitely understand the truth behind that now. As we drove to Target, I was smiling and playing with her daughter, distracting myself from my nervousness. I was scared but wanted to show her I could be tough and I could handle this.

When we pulled up, she told me what to do and told me where she would be parked. This particular Target had a large escalator and it felt like it was moving super slowly. When I finally reached the top and headed to the pharmacy, I noticed the Head Pharmacist was on the phone. Maybe it was the bright orange shirt I was wearing, but he looked up and stared at me for a minute. Long enough to make me uncomfortable. There were about two people ahead of me, and ironically, by the time it was my turn, the Head Pharmacist summoned me to his area. He asked for my name and ID and went back to a phone further back. He made a quick phone call and returned swiftly with the prescription. I paid for it, thanked him, and proceeded to the escalator.

When I approached the escalator, there were about four officers at the bottom. I immediately assumed someone was shoplifting and they were about to grab them. As I got closer to the bottom, I noticed each of them staring me down intensely. *"Oh my goodness, they are waiting for me!"* I felt faint but tried to keep my cool. "Hi, Brittney. Can you come with us please? They surrounded me and began the apprehending process. *"Be tough, be cool, you can do this,"* I said as I walked to the police car. "How old are you, Brittney?" The officer asked politely. "Twenty-three, Sir" "Do you have identification on you?" "Yes Sir, I do" "Ok, Ms. Brittney, we are going to put these handcuffs on you and have you sit in the car and explain what's about to happen." "Sir, what is going on? Am I under arrest? What is happening?" "Let's get to the car and get you situated first. Just relax and walk with me." I fought back the tears, but I knew what was happening. *This was the end.*

The officer was very nice and explained that I was under arrest for picking up a forged prescription for a controlled substance. He asked me where I worked, and who I was here with. I told the truth about where I worked, but lied about who I was with, I told them I was there alone. I knew India had her daughter in the car and I wanted to protect them.

The officer got firm and said, "Brittney, we know you aren't here alone. Just like we know you didn't forge the prescription you just picked up. You gotta tell me the truth and we can work all this out together." I realized then they had probably been expecting me and had seen us pull up. I told him I was here with my aunt and niece. He asked me where they parked, and I said I didn't know. The loud police radio assaulted my ears and I heard them say the make and model of India's car. "Your aunt's car is white, right?" "Yes". "Ok give us a second." He closed the police car door and I panicked, crying like a newborn baby.

Five minutes went by, and I saw India pulling up to where we were. She was being followed by another police car. She got out of the car and started talking to the officers. She told them she would cooperate, but she just needed to call someone to come get her daughter and the car. They honored her request and officially put us under arrest.

When India got in the car, she mumbled, "Say you take it, for recreational purposes, okay and stop crying, it's going to be alright." "Say I take it?!" We waited for her daughter to get picked up and when I saw who came, I wanted to die right then and there. For as long as Heat and I had known each other, I had never met his mother. Now, her first encounter with me was as I sat in the back of a police car. "This was not happening! This was not real!" She was staring in the car at us but kept talking to the officers trying to get to the bottom of what was actually going on. After she transferred India's daughter to her car, we were off to the Police Department to be booked.

Two weeks prior to this happening, I had started a new job in Santa Monica. I was supposed to report to work that evening as well as to my day job. Being booked was uncomfortable and surely not anything I was prepared for. While it was only a holding cell situation, I was behind bars and petrified. I didn't know what to do. I didn't want to call work and I couldn't stomach calling my parents. So, when given my phone call, I chose to call Heat. "Brittney, what the f*** man?! I told your a**, I told you man, f***!!!" The disappointment in his voice killed me. I begged him to call my parents and tell them I was okay, and just staying the night with India. He didn't want to make the call and flat out refused to lie to them.

We were placed across from each other, and India kept

mouthing for me to stay calm and that everything was going to be ok. We had pay phones in our cells. I stared at mine. My parents were the last people I wanted to call. Exhausted from all the crying and the stress of it all, I tried to go to sleep. It was ice cold in there. I had on leggings and a t-shirt. It was dirty, dark, and had this unidentifiable smell that caused my stomach to turn.

I closed my eyes and tried to rest under the thin wool blanket that was provided. The mattress was a joke; I was better off sleeping on the floor. I had finally gotten to a resting point when I heard a lot of commotion from the cell next to me. Drunk people - screaming, fighting, and acting a plum fool. The officers finally got them to quiet down, and I tried to get back to resting. The next thing I heard was, "India, wake up, you've made bail." Ok, some hope was restored. I should be getting bailed out shortly, also. She wouldn't leave me here like this.

Hours went by and I heard nothing. I realized it was the

next day because "breakfast" was slid under the small opening of my cell. Ok, I have to do something. The meal consisted of an almost bad apple, warm apple juice box, and a sandwich with what seemed to be egg on it. Since I was a child, I never liked eggs. I had a traumatic experience with my aunt, where I was force fed some disgusting version of eggs and cold grits because I had declined the meal. I've never liked eggs since. So, I didn't eat. Lunch and dinner were no better, and I was starting to feel the effects of my intentional starvation. My body dysmorphia was so severe that I was actually happy that I didn't have the comfort of food. My thoughts immediately went to losing weight and "becoming beautiful."

I stayed in that cell for five days. My parents bailed me out in the nick of time. One more day and I would have been transferred to the infamous "Twin Towers" to await arraignment. God had favored me. During my short stint, a detective came to question me. He told me that if I had any hopes of getting out of there, I needed to tell him the truth. He assured me that they didn't want me or India, but the person higher than us. *"What person?"* There wasn't a person, or at least, I had no knowledge of them. Referring to me as small fish in a pond full of bigger ones, he leveled with me and told me what I was facing...8 years. EIGHT YEARS! I was barely making these few days, so I knew I wasn't going to make it for any length of time. I told him the truth, never saying what India asked me to say. My entire psyche was distorted and all the "street code" s*** left me. She was back, the scared little girl I had worked so hard to release; but had she ever left? I had nothing to do in jail but reflect and worry. Brittney Baker was now known for fraud and dealing drugs...at 23 years old. Mom and Dad were very angry but also very happy to see me. They took me straight to McDonalds after all the yelling subsided.

I spoke to India a few days after I got home, and

apologies flooded the conversation from both ends. She knew my heart and I knew hers. We did our best to maintain our bond, but that was short lived. Every day I regret not speaking up and telling her no, but I couldn't change any of it, now. That experience taught me the biggest lesson ever, be true to yourself. If you aren't from the streets, don't pretend to be. If you aren't a fighter, don't say you are. Being your true authentic self is the only way you will survive this vicious world.

The wait for court was pure hell. India and I were officially sentenced and got off with fines and probation, no jail time. It was time to make a move. Being in California was not for me anymore. It represented too much hurt, so I gave myself permission to run. But to where? East Coast? Purple begged me to come start over out there. Her whole family rooted for me to head that way, but I wasn't sure. Weeks had gone by, and I was in full on research mode but said nothing to my family. I began my shedding process. When I voluntarily repossessed my car, my parents suspected something was up, but thought it was just a financial move. I literally was a zombie for a few weeks as I caught public transportation and rides from friends.

When Asia called me to vent about all she was going through, and said she needed me out there, my mind shifted, and I began to consider the South. The connection to Heat would still be there and that bothered me a lot, but also gave me hope that we may reconcile. No matter what transpired, he was still the love of my life. I envisioned our future together vividly, and often. Asia was super convincing, but I wasn't sold yet. I enjoyed having the two options, but I knew what it would look like if I chose the South. I told her my reservations about her family, what they might think and say, and what position that would put her in. "I don't care, and you shouldn't either. I need you NieceyPooh. We need each other."

After another week passed, I quietly made my decision. I was moving to Arkansas. I had no clue what would happen next, but I was ready for a change. I lined up job interviews for the next few weeks and closed out all I needed to, in California. My boss at my day job was amazing and agreed to allow me to work remotely until I got on my feet. This came in handy because, financially, I had no idea what I was going to do. Asia, of course, told me not worry about a place to stay. She had plenty of room for me and had reliable transportation as well.

I quietly plotted my departure; waiting until the week before I was supposed to leave to break the news to my family. Dad stopped speaking to me. Mom was overwhelmed and did not know how to process what was happening. Junior was disappointed and hurt. The relationship between me and my niece was getting stronger, and he felt like I was abandoning her as well.

None of this registered, I just needed to go. When I told

Eaglette, she was supportive and begged me not to look back. "If you're going to do this, don't go expecting what you're leaving to follow you there. Let it go friend." Purple was, surprisingly, not upset by my choice and was happy that, at least, I'd be a bit closer to her.

Things were still dark but looking a bit more promising. I was leaving behind everything and everyone I knew. The ride to the airport was uncomfortable. Seeing my mom cry the entire drive was too much to bear. I almost changed my mind. Dad had come around a bit and even helped me with getting things shipped. Visibly upset, he embraced me tighter than a can of biscuits and said, "Dad loves you. I'm sorry you have to do this. Please be careful baby." In that moment, I understood his need to be accountable. He felt responsible for my shortcomings, but I needed him to understand, this was all me, not him.

Parenting is tough, and while I felt like I was a good child, I had given my parents a run for their money. This reset would be good for everyone. Off to uncharted territory I went; scared out of my mind.

As my plane prepared for departure, I chuckled at how much karma was a Queen. She is and will remain the biggest gangsta there is. I had caused a lot of heartache to many loved ones and still felt I was exempt from experiencing what I had done, but Queen Karma will laugh in your face and tell you to think again. Karma takes her time and makes sure she strikes when you least expect it. It could be when you are at your best or at your worse. Now, I move different because of her, and I advise everyone do the same. Queen Karma will always reign.

My eyes were so puffy from crying, they could barely stay open. Yet, I mustered enough strength to keep them open as we flew over my foundation. Bye Inglewood. It's been   real.

Chapter 5 Arkansas Awakening

Views From The South

Culture shock. Those are the only words I can think of to explain how I felt the first few weeks living in Little Rock. Asia was a woman of her word and treated me with such care upon my arrival. I knew nothing about this place but was happy to be away from all the noise and chaos of Inglewood. Asia's home was beautiful, and I was welcomed with open arms by her, her daughters, and boyfriend.

Second week there, I hit the ground running. I had lined up two interviews. Landed the job at the first one and was proud of myself. It was at a popular hotel, and I was excited to be doing what I loved. The pay wasn't the best, but I was thankful to have a job. Next, will be transportation and then my own home. I gave myself 90 days. Asia told me I was insane and could stay with her as long as I needed. However, I was very accustomed to having my own and yearned for it desperately. Her daughters, Summer and Autumn, were the absolute best, especially the older one. When I first met her, she was super reserved and barely liked talking to anyone.

Summer and Autumn were polar opposites. Summer, oddly enough, started gravitating towards me and it made me feel special. Things went from "Summer is so hard to communicate with," to "Brittney, talk to Summer. She'll listen to you." I adored these beautiful young ladies so much but felt like I was infecting them. I felt like my life was on the brink of being over and they were watching me fight for redemption. I didn't think there was anything to admire, but they showed me otherwise, every day. Asia would tell me some of her challenges with them, but I still only saw sweet young girls coming into their own. They were bright spirits, with zero cares in the world. On my harder days, hearing them coming in from school, ready to tell me about their day brought all the joy I needed.

Asia was tough on me about gaining my strength back. She wouldn't let me wallow in depression. She loved her nephew and never talked bad about him but would always encourage me to move forward because she knew he would. She had a photo of him and his first love in her hallway. He'd shared stories with me about her, and I knew what she meant to him. I had to walk past it every day and always stared at it.

One day, I didn't notice where Asia was sitting, and was heading towards the hallway, I stopped and marveled at the photo of my first love with his first love. I was startled by Asia's firm voice, "Ah-Ah! Don't do that. You're bigger than that. Never compare yourself to anyone and never forget the power you possess. Stop torturing yourself." I was ashamed that she'd caught me, and immediately burst into tears. Nothing else needed to be said. I had to really do the work to heal from this. I found myself praying for Heat, often, during this time. I could only imagine the emotions he was feeling behind the whirlwind that was us. *"Focus Brittney…focus."*

Being in Little Rock became easier and easier. I started to learn my way around and to enjoy certain foods. I even allowed Asia and Issac to convince me to join them on a date, occasionally. That was always an epic fail, but I still tried.

I was on track to beating my 90-day goal but decided to add some additional income and reduce the timeframe to 60 days instead. Asia knew what my goals were and never requested a dime from me. Anything I could do for them I would, but she always refused my money. Finally, I had saved up enough money and it was time to make some choices. While I wanted my car first, my own place was calling my name. I moved to the opposite side of town; far from everyone and everything. Asia had lived in that area before and was comfortable with me being there.

The move created a transportation issue, though. I now had 2 jobs and no car. Asia had two cars, but Issac drove one of them. She'd never worried about me using hers to get to work because I would always be back by the time she needed to go. I needed to figure out something quick. Issac was always nice to me, but right before I moved, I noticed some changes in his attitude. It wasn't always towards me but directed to everyone. Of course, like every couple, him and Asia had disagreements and unnecessary drama, but I had managed to stay clear of it. Asia allowed me to continue to use one of her cars, until I could buy one of my own. This caused a bit of a strain between her and Issac, so I needed to change that quickly.

Moving into my new place was the most amazing experience ever. It was 2-bedrooms, 2 baths, and felt like luxury. I didn't have anything, in terms of furniture, and couldn't afford it, yet. What I did have, was a revised heart and a change in how I viewed my life. My air mattress, a couple sofas, and tables we had grabbed from the side of the road, was more than enough for now.

My second bedroom stayed empty, of course. When looking for places, one-bedrooms cost almost the same as two-bedrooms, so why not get the extra space? Asia told me it didn't make sense, but my heart told me I wanted a space for my family, if they came to visit. I also wanted Summer and Autumn to have another safe space, and it could potentially be a workspace for whatever business venture I decided to pursue. Aside from the house in Palmdale, all my apartments were one-bedrooms, so this felt different. It felt like an accomplishment.

Jobs in the hospitality industry were easy to get during that time, so whenever I saw a better opportunity, I'd jumped at it. It was during one of those switches that I met Pickles. Literally the day we met, she introduced herself by saying, "Hey I'm Pickles. You're new here, you're a Black woman, and we're going to be friends, okay?" I was shocked by her forwardness, and a little skeptical as well, but knew I needed to make friends. She took me under her wing and we bonded fairly quickly. It felt like we had been friends for years. She was loyal, dependable, and the sweetest person ever. When she found out that I didn't have a car, she let me use hers as well which relieved some of the stress from using Asia's.

Pickles was younger than me and super accomplished. She attended a prestigious university and was a hard worker. We became inseparable and eventually she moved into my apartment so she could be closer to the city. I finally got a car and was rocking and rolling. It was a true piece of crap, but it was *my* piece of crap. I was overwhelmed with joy at how well this new beginning was going. Little Rock was becoming my new foundation. Everything was aligning in my favor.

My family was dealing with my departure well but still checked on me frequently. Every time I started to miss home, I would remember the disaster I left, and, over time, I grew resentful of my birthplace. Probation and community service still lingered over my head but, thankfully, I was able to make arrangements to complete both in Arkansas and had some time before anything was due to the courts. Pacing myself, I embraced this stage of my healing and continued to find the joy in each day

Steeling Hearts

Asia loved playing matchmaker and it drove me crazy. She tried to introduce me to every man she knew. Every time a call started with, "Ok, so he's not my nephew, but..." I knew she was trying to ask me to go on a date with some random man she felt would be perfect for me.

Heat and I hadn't spoken in a very long time but had broken our silence via messages a while back. We still had our AIM accounts and never removed each other from the contacts list. He often left cryptic lyrics as his away messages and I would do my best to figure out what he was up to by analyzing them, all without reaching out. One evening, he sent me a direct message with lyrics, and I had no idea what it meant. The confusion was back. I asked him to explain, but he never did. It didn't matter. I was just happy to have an open line of communication with him.

I had been gone maybe about 8 months and needed to see my family. I planned a quick weekend trip but kept it a secret from my parents. Through everything, Karlton and I had remained friends, so when I mentioned that I was coming home, he, of course, asked me to make sure that we linked up. I was hesitant at first, but then I agreed. The week before I was set to leave, more messages started to come in from Heat. Nothing promising just simple conversation. He was still very distant, but it restored my hope for reconciliation.

I landed in Ontario, the flight was cheaper, and rented a 3-row SUV to drive to the city. I was nervous and full of anxiety. The moment I reached Inglewood, I felt heavy and disgusted. Still, surprising my family was the absolute best! Mom cried and embraced me for a very long time. Dad being his typical self, said "Well, glad your a** ain't dead yet, Miss Banging in Little Rock," referencing an old documentary about the infamous city. My brother was happy to see me smiling again and my niece had gotten so big.

The following day I arranged to see everyone: my boss, whom I was still working for remotely, Eaglette, Karlton, Heat, and even Nintendo. When I went to pick everyone up, my nerves were rattled. Heat approached the car and went straight to the back seat, saying someone else should ride up front with me. My soul left my body. I was embarrassed and now an emotional wreck in front of all these men.

He was cold and jaded and so not the love of my life. He held his "I give zero f****" face for the entire gathering. That dose of reality hit me hard. He really didn't want me anymore. I was now his past. He was very cordial but barely spoke to me. *"Why agree to come if you didn't want to see me?"*

He kept talking to the guys about an old school pair of shoes that he wanted to bring out of retirement, the Nike

Cortez. He had impeccable style and knew he could make them hot again. Taking a mental note, I remembered that as we ended the evening.

As you grow, you start to see how much respecting peoples wishes is important. Heat had set a boundary and was forcing me to respect it. This was a hard pill to swallow because of my great deal of faith, and hope, in our love. However, God spoke to me on that trip and helped me realize that it was time to let him go. Still wanting him to know that I would always love him, I found the shoes and took them to him before I left. I followed that up with a lengthy message, pouring out my heart and saying my final goodbye. Heat was gone and so was the fairytale I had painted for us.

When I got home to Little Rock, it was back to business as usual. Work, work, work, and more work. I kept trying out different jobs in hopes of figuring out which one would work best for me. Pickles had recently fell head over heels for her first love and was in a life whirlwind, too. She was invested in that, but also in making sure I was okay. However, eventually, she ended up moving back into her old apartment. Our bond stayed tight, but we had to fight to find a good balance from afar.

Asia and I had not spoken since I returned, so when she called me, I thought it was just to check in. "NieceyPooh, there is this really nice young man I want you meet." My eyes immediately began to roll as far back as they could go. "His name is Steele and he is so perfect for you." "Auntie, I'm going to be single for a while. I know you want me to be with someone, but I'm good being alone. "No, you are a Queen who deserves her King. It hurts me that you and my nephew didn't work out, so let me do this, please." "Auntie, I love you, but I'll never love anyone like I did your nephew, and I just want time to heal." "Oh well, you'll have to heal later. I showed Steele your picture and already gave him your number. He's going to call you." *"She'd done what?!"* I was so frustrated. *"Why me God?"*

Within a week, I got a text message from Steele introducing himself. "Hey Brittney! Your Aunt gave me your number. You're so beautiful. She says you aren't from here, and if you want, I can show you around some time." Nervous, I told him I'd think about it, but, in the meantime, we could talk on the phone from time to time.

That was beyond a greenlight for him and he went for it every day. He had a southern accent that I had become accustomed to, but still thought was dreamy. He was assertive and very confident which made him exceptionally attractive to me before I'd even laid eyes on him. His texts weren't the typical "Good Morning. How are you?" messages. They were bigger and deeper. "Did you laugh today?" or "Have you told yourself you're an amazing spirit today?"

Of course, I knew it was all game, but I didn't care. I

entertained him this way for a month before finally agreeing to meet him. I invited him to my place, which is a horrible thing for a single woman, living alone, to do. But, I felt comfortable there and had weapons hidden all over the apartment.

From the moment he pulled up, I was in awe. This tall, dark, skinny, impossibly attractive man approached me with the biggest smile on his face. My heart melted and I fought back my girlish emotions and tried to make it through our first exchange without sounding foolish. When I invited him in, he touched my hand and indicated that I should lead the way. Sparks flew immediately. It was the sexiest thing I'd ever experienced.

I sat at the far end of the sofa hoping he would give me space to collect myself. When he came and sat so close that he was practically on my lap, I got uncomfortable and began to panic. "Look, I'm not here for sex," he reassured me, "I'm just trying to get to know you. You're more beautiful in person than your picture and I can't help but want to be close to you." Whew! G-A-M-E, ALL GAME! But, it was working because I relaxed and started to enjoy his company. We had the best time talking about everything, and nothing, that evening.

Steele was different, and different was what I needed. As our friendship grew so did his feelings for me, and he made me aware of it every opportunity he got. "I want to be with you. I need to be with you. Just say the word and I am yours."

What I enjoyed most about him is how safe I felt when we were together. I didn't think I would feel safe with anyone ever again, but he changed my mind. Still, I was conflicted about moving forward, and I shared that with him. He knew about my breakup and had shared that he had gone through a similar situation in his last relationship. It felt good to be able to relate to someone, in that regard. We complemented each other and I slowly started envisioning myself with him.

When we met, Steele was staying with a friend and was in between jobs. He had a heart condition that had flared up right before and caused a lot of destruction in his life. He was under a lot of stress but when we were together, he felt none of that. Instead of realizing that I was repeating history, I gleefully signed up to be, and embraced being, savior...again. He felt like a breath of fresh air and seemed to be my savior, so I didn't mind.

Steele was the epitome of a "southern gentleman." Doors we held opened for me, I was showered with gifts, and he offered all of himself to me. All the boxes were checked. Plus, he had a relationship with his family, and spoke with them often. He never shied away from telling them about me, and affectionately referred to me as his "soon to be ole lady". He wanted me to meet his family right away, but I declined. I had no idea what we were becoming, so I avoided it.

Sex was also a constant topic of discussion between us, which was very weird because I am not a very sexual person. His hormones were raging, and he always expressed his yearning for my body. We'd be having dinner or watching a movie and he'd randomly blurt out, "Let's wrap this up, because you have no idea how bad I want to take you down right now." He'd beg me to "turn down the sexy" when we saw each other because it was hard for him to resist the temptation. This brought out a confidence in me, I never knew I had. Over time, not being outspoken had caused me to only listen to my negative inner voice and view of myself. I never thought highly of myself, even as my confidence was being forcefully developed.

Steele and I moved fast, but it was a perfect pace in my opinion. I thought about Heat less and less, and truly wanted to be in love again. During that time, nothing mattered except our relationship. As much experience as I had gained from being with Heat, the lessons still hadn't been learned.

Steele and I grew more and more in love. He gazed at me endlessly, spoke to, and about, me with an explosive passion, and never missed an opportunity to spend time with me. When one was as inexperienced as I was at the time, these were more than highlights; they were golden tickets to an unattainable love story. I was blown away by how he made me feel.

His public and private admiration made me weak to my core. He stole my heart with his corny jokes, random questions, and unwavering investment in my happiness. I tried hard not to compare my past experiences with my current situation but couldn't help myself. Steele told me he loved me, first, and even explained why. This exchange erased my uncertainty and made me trust him completely. I believed him and our love.

Pickles was not a fan of Steele. In her opinion, the over-the-top affection was a mask for something he was hiding. Her strong opinion was heard but ignored. "Something about this n**** don't sit well with me," she would say repeatedly. Asia was excited to see me in love, again, and proudly took credit for the union. My family did not take me seriously when I told them about Steele. Although they'd had reservations about Heat, they really loved him, and had been rooting for us to work things out. Bringing another man into the equation was not ideal, but they accepted it. Being miles away, they didn't get to experience Steele the way I did, but I sang his praises daily. Steele was my future, and I was proud of that.

Listening to friends and family when you're in love can be tricky and the strength of their influence can alter how you handle your significant other. This go round, I wanted to make sure I was following only *my* heart and mind.

Glimpse of Destruction

Steele was a risk taker. I loved that about him. We had been together for over a year and fell more in love each day. When he brought up going to the military, I was sad and nervous about his, out of the blue, choice. Military meant relocating, greater distance from my family, and a life I just wasn't sure I was ready for. His heart and mind were made up. He studied everything about the military and prepared himself to enlist. While I was supportive, I was still very unsure of what that meant for us.

One evening he called me at work and said, "I'm not enlisting until you are my wife, I won't do it without you. Besides, the benefits are better when you're married." I laughed hysterically, "Wife? Boy stop playing with me. You're not asking me to marry you." "Actually, I am, Brittney. I love you! I won't do this any other way…marry me?" He was serious, and the idea of it all gave me goosebumps. *"Twenty-four years old and married?"* Didn't even sound right in my head, never mind saying it out loud. This was a big choice and I had lots to consider before I could give him an answer.

When I got home that evening, Steele did a formal proposal, but with no ring, just pure love from his heart and soul. His actions, and his confidence in our love, gave me the courage to believe and move forward. So, the answer was yes, and we went on a quest to become husband and wife.

We were smitten with the idea of marriage without a clue about the work we had just signed up for.

The idea of marriage is always prettier than the
reality of it. Being infatuated with each other is one
thing but deciding to become one takes more than just
a single conversation.

We rode down the road to marriage without training wheels, deciding to figure it out as we went along. First step, a huge move - relocating to Dallas, Texas. The military opportunities were plentiful out there and perfect for us to start our newlywed life together. So that was the plan, get to Texas, get married, and live happily ever after.

God has a way of sending you warning shots, and it's up to you to receive them. I ignored them, proudly. While Steele's love for me was obvious, his deceitfulness played peek-a-boo often, and that bothered me. Also, his need to be entertained outside our home began to detract from my admiration for him. Accusations of infidelity arose, and it was clear things weren't totally aligned. I was never able to fully prove anything I just felt like he had cheated. All I could do was live with my painful intuition. I quickly blamed it on stress and the pressure that trying to join the military was putting on him. The move to Texas was going to be our fresh start. Also, subconsciously, I felt like I could and would change things for us.

Let's be clear, love does conquer all, but it cannot

change who a person is at their core. This lesson was a difficult one to grasp. I still struggle with it to this day. Change needs to be desired, and in my opinion, can't be taught. We can all learn how to adjust, but that is simply the temporary mask we wear. In the darkest of hours, who are you? Do you really want the improvement being requested of you, or are you doing it because you feel like you have no choice?

Steele and I pushed forward with our plans, and I continued to find hope and peace in everything. We were celebrating the 4th of July with his family, when I got a phone call from a wedding officiant. While things weren't the best, we still wanted to have our moment, and I was in full on planner mode. I had made tons of calls inquiring about the process and kept getting the run around. Shocked to be getting the call on a holiday, I expressed that I was in the planning stage and was just trying to gather information. "Do you love him?" "Yes, of course I do."

"Then meet me at the courthouse in an hour." We had no rings, no plan, just pure love, faith, and hope. We left the gathering and were officially married within the hour.

Steele and I had very little money, but lots of faith. I was the only one working and our plan was to drop everything and start over completely in Texas. Things were rough, but we had high hopes and a clear plan. We even had the nerve to get a dog. Hotel jobs would be easy to secure in Texas, and Steele would work diligently to complete his enlistment. Then, he ran into an issue due to his visible facial tattoo and it derailed everything.

It was around that time that his temper began to flare intensely. Our verbal sparring became routine and mean. The physical abuse showed up suddenly and swifter than the iceberg that sank the Titanic. Honestly, at first, I wasn't even sure if I was actually being abused. The attacks began very subtly - a push here, a face nudge there - small things that didn't seem like a big deal. Growing up, Junior had done those same things to me, often, so I didn't immediately connect it to being abused. Plus, I was from Inglewood. I was expected to be tough and sassy. I was raised to defend myself, but never prepared for it to be against a man.

Domestic violence is such a taboo topic and no matter your upbringing, you never know how you will handle it until you experience it.

"Fight a man?! Was I even capable of that?" I thought about telling my dad or my brother but realized that may escalate things. They'd risk their freedom for me.

Pushing buttons wasn't always intentional but my mouth was slick, and I knew exactly what to say to hurt Steele. I tried to tread lightly, but when provoked, I would unleash a "Brittney Tongue Lashing", like no other. So, when the abuse started getting worse, I simply blamed myself. Even though, there were times when his outbursts were unwarranted and came out of nowhere. I was scared.

I knew how bad he could hurt me, so I took the blows, while I was quietly dying inside.

Texas was OVERWHELMING. While full of excitement, I had gone out there with a mixture of heavy heart and high hopes. The abuse and being so far away from home made me feel empty and hopeless. I was alone and literally felt like all I had was my dog. The world would never know that though. I made it my mission to show only my highlight reel. Disguising my pain with smiles and laughter. I poured myself into work. I was working two jobs during our transition and preferred it that way. The few hours I spent at home and my limited off days were numbed by eating good food to try and avoid falling into depression.

Infidelity shook my world unexpectedly, and slammed into my heart like a jackhammer, when I made an unfortunate discovery about Steele. He'd been communicating with a Texan woman and things were apparently getting serious. She had found out where I worked and my schedule. When she asked for me, I was for certain she was a hotel guest looking for assistance. After confirming who I was, she instantly started spewing her truth and offering me intimate details about my husband.

Here I was, married to this man, cautiously avoiding his temper, and doing my best to keep our heads above water. This was the last thing I expected. Done. My heart was done. Not only was this information hard to accept, but I was angry that I had let it happen again! She explained that he was becoming a bit obsessive, and she wanted it to stop. This woman was pleading with me to make my husband leave her alone. Without a plan or even thinking it through, I decided to follow my gut. *"Leave Brittney; leave him."*

My attempt to express my hurt, was quickly drowned out by Steele's overwhelming remorse and shocking threat on his life. He told me that if I left him, he no longer wanted to live. A loud, shattering, noise reverberated in my ears and all I could hear was my dog barking. "Steele, Steele? Hello?" *"Oh no! What had he done?"* I left work and headed straight for home. My adrenaline was sky high, and I was panicked. *"Should I call the police?"*

When I arrived at our residence, I found Steele on the ground surrounded by a broken glass bottle and a knife. He had been crying and his eyes were bloodshot. He was shaking and seemingly in a daze. He was conscious, but not being coherent. The person I loved was contemplating harming himself and I was mortified! I felt like he knew, subconsciously, how I would react. Knew that I would never forgive myself if something bad actually happened to him. Just a few weeks before, he'd begged me to buy him a firearm for protection. Due to our history, I was nervous about having a gun in the house and pretended we couldn't afford it. Truth is, I was scared it would get used on me, and now I was glad because he could've use it on himself.

Love overpowered everything. We both fought hard to reconcile our marriage. He started communicating better and expressing his thoughts clearly. I began to acknowledge my role in our demise and understood that I also had not been the best mate. While my fear of the violence had caused me to avoid being home, my absence had created a great sense of emptiness in him.

When you are in the thick of things, you never see it

the other person's way.

I was the victim in my eyes; I was the one being abused. However, I was inflicting mental abuse, and never realized the weight it added to our relationship. So, I loved harder and showed up more. We learned a lot about each other during that time as we supported each other through the gruesome healing process.

The military did not pan out the way we anticipated,

and Steele ultimately chose to go in another direction. When he finally got a job, things changed for the better. He was excited, and so was I. I'd pack his lunch, iron his clothes, and praise him as often as I could. Being able to contribute financially changed him. He was kind, sweet, thoughtful, and focused. Texas was no longer feeling like a mistake.

I reduced my work hours but was still working two jobs. Feeling fatigued was common, but I was beyond that. My body ached, and I always felt ill. I ignored it, but my heart told me something was wrong, physically. When you experience life changing circumstances it's important to check on your vessel. I, regrettably, did not but fought through the pain, instead.

When my health started to decline, I did my best to keep it from everyone. Having Turner Syndrome, I'd grown accustomed to hiding the battles. I never wanted sympathy. However, whatever was going on with me started to show up persistently. Constant nausea, fatigue, weight gain, shortness of breath, body aches, and random discharges from my vagina. For someone who'd never had a menstrual cycle, this was new and very uncomfortable.

When I finally went to the doctor, I received unwanted and devastating news. "There is a tumor forming, it's small but looks malignant, so we need to operate soon." "Wait, so are you telling me I have cancer?" "Yes, Ms. Baker you do." My life flashed before my eyes. I thought of everyone and everything. *"God, I'm not done. I know you aren't ready for me yet."*

The medical industry is a business, and I was not in a position to play the games the doctor's wanted to play, so I opted to try holistic remedies on my own before agreeing to the surgery. Still keeping this all to myself, I researched and did my best to heal myself. There were good days and bad days. Steele noticed it all but didn't say much.

One evening, I was in between jobs and needed to

change uniforms. I never really had much time, so I would run in, change, and run out. This particular evening, my body was failing me and producing more discharge than usual. I washed up, changed my undergarments and clothes, and ran out the door. We had a walk-in closet that our dog loved to play in if we left the door open. He would have a field day with shoes and clothes. In my rush to leave, I had left the door partially open.

When I got to the car, I realized I didn't have my work badge and had to go back inside. When I entered, I found our dog with my soiled underwear in his mouth and Steele chasing him. When he retrieved the underwear, Steele's face showed disgust and great concern, simultaneously. "Brittney, are you okay? What's going on? What is this?" I didn't have time nor the energy to explain. I snatched the underwear from him and threw it in the garbage. I was embarrassed and knew he wouldn't understand. It looked like a lazy, overweight, person not taking care of themselves. I figured I'd fight this battle another day and proceeded to go to work.

When I returned home, Steele had cooked a lovely meal, had a bath waiting for me, and simply wanted me to relax. While in the tub, he came and pleaded with me to tell him the truth, so I did. "We have to find you the best doctors and get you all the help you need." His support meant everything to me. When he mentioned telling my parents, I froze. "No. I can't tell them this right now," I cried in agony. "Are you crazy?! They have to know Brittney!" "NO!" I said firmly. "I'm going to be fine; I'll beat this." I had learned to become a vault for a lot of reasons. I knew how to compartmentalize things and felt my way was best. I was so wrong! I needed all the support I could get but refused it behind my pride and sense of being worthless.

Weeks had gone by and the pain had lessened. Steele stayed on me about everything and altered our lifestyle around my health. When I went back to the doctor, the tumor had grown, but not as aggressively as they thought it would have without surgery. "You need radiation" The medical terms, and the costs associated with them, was too much for me. I gave up on getting treated and decided I was going to just live the life I had left, to the best of my ability.

Scared, but fearless, I embraced my faith and found joy in the "little" things. I was scared to talk to God. He had disappointed me, and I didn't know how to say that without seeming ungrateful. So, I said and did nothing.

Steele and I planned a trip to California. He knew I needed to see my family. That trip turned out to be awesome for both of us. Seeing Steele's eyes light up in the airport, while mentally absorbing all that was California, was a reward. We left that trip feeling refreshed and refueled. Texas was preparing for a big snow blizzard, when we returned. I went to work as usual, praying I wouldn't get snowed in. That evening was slow at work, and around 2a.m., I sat down and decided to check my email.

"From: Heat

Subject: Hello Texas"

My heart jumped out of my chest. I hadn't heard from him in a while and with a child on the way, Asia had mentioned his girlfriend's pregnancy during one of our conversations, I never thought I would hear from him again. The email was simply a check-in; nothing inappropriate or out of the ordinary. In the follow-up messages, he didn't pry too much, but it was clear that he knew things about me. Our exchange was healthy and left me filled with sweet memories.

I risked the drive home. The snow was sticking, but I felt I could make it. Steele always talked to me on the drive to and from work, so us being on the phone wasn't uncommon. The subject matter made this conversation a bit different, though. Since we were in such a good place, I needed to be honest with him and told him about the conversation with Heat. The discussion got heated and I wasn't fully focused on the road. Out of nowhere, a car from the opposing traffic lost control, ran dead smack into me, which caused me to spin out of control, colliding with three more cars before stopping. I was knocked unconscious. The last thing I remember was Steele screaming my name as I yelled "Oh my God!"

When I woke up, I was strapped to a gurney in the back of an ambulance. Blood was everywhere and Steele was staring at me, face full of tears, gripping my hand tight. I tried to speak, but he shushed me and told me I was in a bad accident, and I should save my energy. I noticed he was not fully dressed which raised so many questions. I found out later, that when the accident happened, Steele had no idea where I was on my drive home, but knew I was a creature of habit, so he was able to give the first responders my exact route. Turns out I was only 2 miles away from home. He had darted out of the house so quickly to find me, he hadn't had time to get dressed. I'm still in awe of his quick thinking which saved my life that day. I had suffered a concussion, bruised ribs, and severe whiplash and was hospitalized for 6 days but God was merciful and had spared me.

During my hospitalization, all hell broke loose. Our jobs weren't understanding, the car was totaled, and we had no back up plan. We were able to secure a rental car through the insurance company, but that was only for a limited time. I was let go from one of my jobs and Steele was given less hours at his. The darkness was forming again. Being in Texas without a car was not a good thing. Everything was far and spread out and public transportation was limited. On top of all that, I was still sick. We just couldn't get ahead.

While it would have been ideal to move back home to California, my heart couldn't stomach it. Heat's child was about to arrive, and while the information I had received was very limited, it stayed on my mind, constantly. I even sent him a gift for his unborn bundle of joy. It was my wish that the love I had for him and held space for would spew over to his seed and his significant other. Being selfless comes with severe heartache, but I experienced it all knowing it made him happy, and more importantly, knowing his creation would be too.

Ultimately, Steele and I decided to make our way back to Arkansas, and start over there. Asia was kind enough to let us stay with her for a few weeks until I found a job. She even let us borrow one of her vehicles until we could figure out our situation completely. Then there was a shift in our friendship, that I honestly wasn't prepared for. She became dark, mean spirited, and short tempered. Issac was now her husband, and things were just off. I knew we couldn't stay with her very long.

Steele was feeling completely defeated and had shut

down. His motivation to work, or do anything for that matter, seemed non-existent. The pressure to fix every detail of my life was beyond heavy. When I started a new job, the newly promoted manager gravitated towards me.

Tiffany was an older, church going, woman who read spirits and energy frequently. I kept my smile most days, but there were times when the physical and mental pain would engulf me. Those days were harder to get through, but I managed and did my best to stay focused. Tiffany was very observant, and caught me crying and praying one day during my daily walk around the property.

Have you ever had someone ask you what's wrong, and have no words, just inaudible sound, tears, and a release of frustration? Tiffany saw me crying, hands to the sky, clenched with hopelessness and frustration. She approached me saying four words, "How can I help?" Explaining my situation was not easy, but I tried my best that afternoon.

Tiffany had a solution, instantly. "Room 4307 is out of order for 30 days because of that backordered mirror and headboard. Stay in there until you can secure your place. I'll get approval, don't worry. You can stay for at least 3 weeks." Working in hospitality has its perks, but I hadn't seen this blessing coming. Steele and I moved into the room. Living in a hotel was not ideal, but convenient and I was just happy for a quick solution to my issue.

We returned Asia's car, and things began to really fall apart between her and I. It was painful watching our relationship deteriorate. I tried not to take it personally, and just governed myself accordingly. She was dealing with a lot and had many battles to fight; I didn't want to be one of them. I stayed distant but did my best to still keep an open line of communication. Another failed friendship was on the horizon, and I was devastated. *"Why couldn't I sustain anything?"*

Steele got a job, and we were able to move into our own

space. The physical violence showed up, again. This time, more intense and dangerous. He was so powerful and as much as I tried to defend myself, I could never win the fights. I resorted back to thinking I deserved it. Blaming myself for every punch thrown and every foul word exchanged.

Truth is, no matter the situation, we had no way of managing the toxic magnet we possessed.

When the red flags show up, you must pay attention.

They can ultimately save your life.

I feared for my life often but overcompensated for that emotion with love and thoughts of a potentially bright future. Sometimes your peace is also your headache. Steele was worn down; life had truly done a number on him. I felt I could remedy that.

For most abused women, we live our life in three phases. Denial: we acknowledge our partner's abusive traits but refuse to accept that it's happening to us. Acceptance: we develop deep, mentally twisted, forgiveness for our abuser's actions and justify it frequently. Then there is retaliation: this is where we fight back and fear no repercussions.

Steele and I were not in a good place and my illness did not make matters any better. We fought like cats and dogs. I was always shocked at how far we'd go in each argument or fight. He became a villain, and I became a woman of rage. Being abused will change you completely. I was always on guard and stayed prepared to defend myself. That pressure was heavy, but it was my reality.

As my illness progressed, I finally decided to get the surgery. The resources and access to healthcare were different in Arkansas and made the process easier. Preparing for surgery was hard. I was nervous, and still battling so many demons. The process was gruesome, test after test, visit after visit, call after call. I was exhausted by the time the date rolled around. Trying to keep it all a secret was also a big challenge. I even lied to Steele a few times about appointments and small details. When I finally secured the surgery date, I felt relieved but still so uncertain.

Steele and his mother took me to the hospital the day of the surgery. His display of love for me overshadowed all our bad experiences. He was so attentive, patient, and concerned. He got on everyone's nerves that day. There were particular stages in my surgery prep that he couldn't be a part of, and it bothered him tremendously. The nurses thought it was the sweetest thing. He paced, asked questions, and demanded to be at my bedside the whole time. They let him see me right before I went under anesthesia. The tears he cried warmed my heart, yet, all I saw was Steele the villain standing next to me. We loved each other deeply but were no good for each other.

The anesthesia hit quick. I remember doing the backwards count, making it to 7, and nothing else. When I woke up the pain was excruciating. The recovery room was bright, and symbolic of what I imagine heaven to be. The nurse explained that the surgery went well and there were no complications.

They let Steele come to see me and he had my parents on the line. "Yes ma'am, she's awake, I don't think she can talk yet, but she can listen." He placed the phone to my ear and allowed me to hear the sweet sounds of my mother's voice. She clearly had been crying and was a ball of emotions. "Hi Babygirl! Mommy is here. I'm so sorry you had to go through this alone. Steele told us everything. Brittney, please come home. I can't stomach this anymore; I need my baby near me; please come home." This conversation followed with the strong, loud tone of my father, "So you done let these people cut on yo a**. I done told you about them damn doctors. We're sending for you. You gotta come home baby." I barely remembered the events of the day and could hardly process the conversation. *"Home? I was home, at least I thought I was."* I felt the life I had built here in Arkansas was meant for me and I didn't want to leave it. After 4 weeks of recovery and several conversations, I made the decision to accept my parent's offer, and leave Arkansas for good.

Saying goodbye to everyone was difficult. Pickles was hurt and didn't really know how to express it. It almost felt like I let her down. Everything happened so suddenly, so I understood. Asia didn't take it well either. "You gotta tell the girls, I'm not." The evening I stopped by to tell Summer and Autumn, they were really somber and not in the best mood. Crying, hugs, and lots of "I love you" transpired, as I did my best to let them know nothing would change because I still loved them very much. Summer said the cutest thing "We'll be like long distance friends." "Yes, exactly!" "I know, I'll call you DF for short." "I want my own name" Autumn stated. "Well, you're my kindhearted baby, so you can be my KDF and Summer will be my LDF." "What about me?" Asia asked. "You've been like a mother to me out here, so you will be "Momma DF" "Yes, I'm Momma DF!" she said gleefully. Having that moment with them cemented our bond and I prayed that it would remain that way after I left Arkansas. Weeks later, Steele and I were packed. We shipped our vehicle and a few things and flew to sunny California

Chapter 6 Contagious California

Mindset Makeover

Moving back home was petrifying. We had to move in with my parents, who already had a house full. The chaos, the worry, the fear of acceptance attacked me all at once. Steele was ecstatic to be in the glorious sunshine state. We were fully embraced by my family and that was refreshing. Life forces you to balance and redirect your focus often and we did just that. Nothing ever changes until our mindsets do. Whether I liked it or not, we were here, and I had to make sure each move going forward was perfect for us.

My niece, Skylar, was practically a teenager and Junior had recently shared the exciting news that he was expecting his second child, Aris. Aris was born under extremely different circumstances than Skylar, and my family wasn't prepared for it. Her mother and Junior were no longer getting along, and that made it difficult for everyone involved. Still, she was an absolutely amazing baby and we were enamored with her.

Drama continued to unfold and watching Junior battle that was painful. As a family, we always sided with Junior, and couldn't really accept the behavior Aris's mother was presenting to us. We all acted immaturely. Later, we discovered that we weren't privy to most of the truth. I had a lot on my plate and adding this didn't help matters. We were too close of a family to have this type of turmoil over a blessing like Aris. Eventually, we concluded that everyone needed to make an effort to get along for her sake.

Having the love and support of my family was beyond beneficial. No one judged me for keeping my illness a secret and the jokes about my past had ceased. The goal now was to build a new foundation and grow with my husband.

Steele and I fell deeper in love which made it easier for me to hold the torch to the finish line. It felt like we were in a legit honeymoon stage. We dated again, talked more candidly, and did our absolute best to create the life we wanted. He'd do simple, but sweet things, like leave a love note in the car we shared, or wake me up by whispering, "I love you" continuously until I was fully awake.

My body had completely changed after surgery. I was heavier due to the medication, had no energy most times, and physical intimacy was difficult. I was over health and beauty, as a whole. Still, he never stopped calling me beautiful and never blamed me for anything that was lacking. I felt truly blessed to have someone who was so understanding, even with all his shortcomings. In my mind, California was helping my marriage. Months passed and we had gotten into a routine. Both Steele and I had found work, and I was grateful.

Winnie and I re-connected, and she was happy that I was home and able to be around my godchildren more. I had taken on a very private mentality and rarely shared the details of my life with her. She knew I was married, but knew nothing about him, and it annoyed her.

Winnie had a great sense of character; she was able to sniff out someone's b******* from miles away. I didn't want to be judged or ridiculed, so I deflected the conversation away from my marriage, often. She never met Heat, but from what she'd heard about him, she read him for filth. There was a fear she would tell me the truth about Steele. What Steele and I were building was uncertain, and I wanted limited distractions. So, I focused on friendship and rebuilding that bond.

Eaglette and I were also reunited and boy, was it magical! She was pregnant with her first child, and we were inseparable. She didn't dislike Steele, but knew he

185

wasn't the best person for me. She supported me anyway.

The transition from Arkansas to California was going smoothly until I got an email from Heat. I'd been preparing myself for this since we landed. Communicating with him always threw me off, but I felt like I needed it. I needed to hear from him to make sure he was doing well. Even though when I did, the space I saved for him in my heart, would always grow larger and I had no idea how to stop it.

Again, trying to be honest and straightforward, I told Steele about the email. Surprisingly, he took it well. My intuition told me he'd prepared himself for the possibility of me seeing or bumping into Heat, eventually, but trusted the strength of my love for him. Scary thing is, I didn't trust it. Loving two people at once is a thing. I was a married woman and felt embarrassed at the thought.

Heat and I made arrangements to meet, grab some food, and catch up. It felt wrong, but I needed to see him;

needed to look in his eyes. Dinner was harmless, but it surely didn't feel like two friends catching up. He was still cold and distant, but more open to sharing his life than he was before. We were "friends" and he made sure to remind me of that every chance he got.

"So y'all went on a date?" Eaglette asked directly. "No, I paid, so technically it wasn't a date." "Right, you keep telling yourself that, alright friend. I hope you are ready for all that comes with this. You're married, this should be a no brainer." "We're just friends," I said. "He's your first love. Give him the correct title and stop trying to convince me otherwise. Did you tell Steele?" "Yes" "Brittney, did you tell Steele you were going to dinner with *Heat*, yes or no?" she persisted. "No. I told him I was going to dinner with an old friend." "Exactly, now you're lying to yourself and to your husband. Do you, but just get ready."

Get ready. That echoed in my ear for weeks. If the tables were turned, I wouldn't be comfortable with Steele doing what I had done, and that was the honest truth. I was a faithful woman, faithful and devoted wife, but my heart belonged to both Heat and Steele. The struggle continued and so did the deceit. I had to make a change and quickly. My thoughts had been consuming me, but it was time to get out of this thick haze of confusion and destruction and take action.

Mindsets are so difficult to change, especially when you are comfortable. Shifting gears is beyond uncomfortable but needed and takes more than thoughts. There are plenty of moments in our lives where we feel the hand we've been dealt is final but that's not necessarily true.

Secrets & Separations

The honeymoon stage of being in California was slowly coming to an end. The pressure of surviving was leading our union, instead of God. More deceit and devils-play crept up on the horizon. Being in my comfort zone changed the way I operated in my marriage. I was no longer scared to fight back and I'm sure that not only surprised, but also infuriated Steele. I was closer to my army of protection and used that to my advantage. I still withheld that portion of our story from my family, but Steele would hear, "I'll make one phone call and you already know what's up" and he understood exactly what that meant. He witnessed the love surrounding me from not only my family, but the friends I had in my corner, as well.

I'd become a manager in the hospitality industry and was excited and extremely proud of my accomplishment. I hadn't thought I was capable of managing a property on my own. There were several different personalities to manage and it was a lot of responsibility. It was gritty, and the politics were insane, but I loved every minute of it. It pulled me away from home and I was missing family gatherings and outings with friends. I didn't realize it but being solely focused on work was an avoidance trait that I was forming. The more I ignored my reality, the easier I thought things would become. Long, hard, hours were required but I did it with a smile. All the while knowing it was a mask.

When I was terminated from that job, I fell into a dark depression. My health declined, I gained a ton of weight, and my spirit was at an all-time low. When you feel as low as I did, optimism is non-existent, and you can see nothing in a positive light. I pulled on every ounce of strength I had and decided it was time for a change. I worked hard to lose weight, find employment, and sustain my health, but it was remarkably challenging.

Steele worked diligently alongside me and was an amazing cheerleader. The phases we experienced during this time felt like the ultimate roller coaster. Ups and downs, twists and turns, but we dealt with it together. I couldn't voice it, but deep down I knew the win would happen eventually.

We all experience these phases in life, and what makes

us powerful during them is how we view ourselves.

As the bills piled up so did my desperation. Then, I was fortunate enough to be blessed with an awesome job opportunity. It started off as a downgrade; I would no longer have the manager title, but if I worked hard enough, I could potentially earn it. When I interviewed with Sasha, the head of the Sales Department, our chemistry was magical. I saw something in her that was beyond special, and she felt the same about me.

Keeping my ego in check was harder than the actual job.

I fought tooth and nail to be "respected" for my skills, yet, was boxed into a role I knew I had surpassed in my career. Sasha humbled me, by letting me know that my work would prove that, not my constant verbal reminders. I loved Sasha's ability to see me and my worth even as she encouraged me to do the grunt work first. She was an amazing leader, and we were perfectly aligned.

My battles with Steele never stopped and would often have my head out of the game. Sasha wouldn't pry, but always offered her time and advice, if I needed it. Special connections are rare, and I didn't realize how blessed I was at that moment, until later. After knowing her less than a year, I was shocked at how comfortable I was sharing things with her. The abuse was something I was too ashamed to talk about, but to this day, I think she always knew. When she had troubles with her significant other, we'd swap stories and she actually listened to my insight and perspective. Knowing that she valued my wisdom made me feel special.

I was also close to the other two team members, Rosarito and Ricardo. The four of us were a powerhouse to be reckoned with and had each other's backs a 1000%! We had our disagreements, but for the most part we were solid in our intentions. This made working together and my downgrade easier to accept.

When Steele and I were blessed with our own space, I instinctively knew things would get worse. Moving into a new space should be exciting, but, for me, it carried a heavy burden of the unknown.

Women who experience abuse live in constant

paranoia, which, ironically, fuels more physical

exchanges.

We had to be discreet in my parents' home. Steele couldn't come home at 3a.m. from a night of partying or randomly decide to curse me out. Meanwhile, I could threaten to leave him or disappear for hours without an explanation.

As soon as we moved, it was almost like he now had permission to live a different lifestyle and dared me to challenge it.

Steele started making more friends and truly becoming his own version of a California native. While I was happy to see him progressing in that area, I knew the price tag would be hefty. What I began to see show up was a wounded man looking to be freed from his pain. The form of release, unfortunately, was through beating up on me.

Eventually, God will start showing you your reality and force you to make a decision. Constant tests, constant changes, nothing was ever just peaceful; it was exhausting.

An exit plan started developing in the back of my mind. It was 3a.m. on a Saturday morning, I had hung out with Eaglette all of Friday night and just couldn't stomach going home. I knew Steele wouldn't be there and seeing that would infuriate me. Eaglette had plans, and while she offered for me to stay with her, I wanted to be alone. This alone felt different though. As I hugged her bye, it felt final. I started crying and she became confused, "B****, are you crying? Alright, come upstairs and lay down; you're tipsy." I assured her I was fine and let her know how much I loved her.

When I was staying at my parents, I became privy to a lot of things they thought I didn't know about. Junior had a lifestyle that he was exiting himself. One that was full of danger and caused him to have a constant need for protection. He thought I didn't know where he kept his weapons, but I did. I left Eaglette's and drove to my parent's. I was on auto pilot, but I knew what had to be done. I snuck in quietly. My Dad was up but wasn't startled by my entry since I frequently dropped by unannounced. He was making his nightly rounds, checking on his home, and would soon return to bed. "You drunk?" he asked gruffly. "No, Dad" "Ok, go to bed. I'll go get you some tamales in a few hours." He loved to feed me; he knew that made me happy. "Ok" I said, knowing I wouldn't be there long.

My Dad never questioned our impromptu visits, he always just let us be. I relied on that heavily that morning. I knew I had a 15-minute window before he'd come and check on me. I'd be gone long before that. The second I heard his door close, I raced to where the weapon was hidden. The gun was loaded, heavy, clean, and shiny. It was oddly beautiful. I chuckled; Junior took care of all his things so well. He was particular about everything. The tears flowed heavily. I was going to miss my brother. I cherished everything he had taught or tried to teach me. He made a lot of mistakes, but he loved me very much, and I knew that.

I didn't mean to be in the situation I was in, I didn't mean to have failed my family with my choices in life, particularly when it came to men, but here we were. *"Get it together Brittney. Just go, get it done already!"* I told myself as I weaseled out of my parents' home. Dad must have been tired, because he didn't notice that I had left the front door ajar, so the alarm wouldn't announce my exit.

The gun was in my purse; wrapped in a towel I had grabbed. Not knowing where I was headed, I hopped on the freeway and just drove. It was creeping up on 5a.m. when I got to Pasadena. I used to work in the area a while back and always felt at peace whenever I entered. There were a lot of businesses, but if you turned off the right street, you'd get an amazing view of the gorgeous mountains surrounding the city.

I was scared and my heart was racing. This was it! All I could think about was the amount of shame and disappointment I had caused my family. My heart was beyond heavy, and I just didn't want to live in this hell anymore. The gun was cold as I positioned it to my temple. My hand was shaking uncontrollably. *"Do you do it on the left or right side?"* I repositioned it - under my chin, this time. I had no blueprint for how to kill myself. Just what I had seen in the movies or heard about from others. I was literally winging it.

I closed my eyes tight and got ready to pull the trigger. Letting out the loudest scream possible, I tried, but couldn't do it. I wanted to, but I couldn't pull the trigger. My parents' faces floated into my mind as my eyes remained clenched shut. I loved them with every ounce of my soul, this would destroy them.

Rocking back and forth, gun still to my chin, I said aloud, "God, please forgive me." I opened my eyes and gently placed the gun in my lap. My eyes were so puffy from crying, that I could barely see, but the sun was rising. I was exhausted. This tug of war had gone on for a while and it was well after 6a.m. at this point. My mind was playing tricks on me, and I needed rest. I had put myself in a very dangerous situation. I put the gun away and closed my eyes for what seemed like 5 minutes, but in reality, was 2 hours. When I woke up, I saw that Dad had called me at least 20 times, so had Steele.

As I drove home an immense amount of gratitude came over me. My life was spared yet again. *"Why was I so lucky? So favored?"* Just before I exited the freeway, I glanced up and saw a billboard. "Divorce is delicate, and we'll handle you with care, call us now for help." *"Divorce?"* That had never crossed my mind. I was in the for the long haul, "til death do us part." I would suffer for this man until I couldn't anymore. Why God chose to have me see that billboard, at that particular moment, will always be a mystery. I made it home and, of course, was interrogated by Steele. He accused me of being with another man, and even brought up Heat. The more he talked, the more I realized I needed to leave this situation, and soon.

No circumstance is worth your beautiful life. While it
may be full of unprecedented events, the life we're

given is a work of art, intended to be carefully curated

by you and your higher power. Find the value in

yourself always.

I got some more rest and woke up a completely different person. My maternal grandmother visited me in my dreams and all she kept saying was "Leave." Nothing else but that one word. I was going to leave Steele. I *had* to leave him.

I had completely forgotten that the gun was in my purse and didn't know how I was going to get it back to my parents' home undetected. Thankfully, they had a schedule I knew like the back of my hand, and I simply had to wait. To my surprise, Junior was there when I arrived, and I had no backup plan. We were very close, so he could always tell when I was up to something. "You seen my gun?" He asked the moment he laid eyes on me. Caught off guard, I quickly lied, "No. What gun?" "Man, I hope Dad didn't find it and hide it. They coming back soon?" "Yes" I quietly responded. He grabbed his mail, gave me a hug, and as he was walking out the door, turned and said, "Put my s*** back." My mouth dropped as he continued to his car. *"How did he know? There was no way he could've known"*. Us being in sync was always an inside joke; with our birthdays being a day apart, we grew up swearing we were twins. There were times when I could feel my brother's pain and vice versa; guess he felt mine that morning.

I still don't know the details of how that morning went. Maybe Dad told him I came by but left suddenly. Maybe Steele called him when he couldn't get a hold of me. Whatever it was, we never discussed it, like many things in our lives, I buried it and so did he.

I was done fighting, done battling for love, I just wanted peace. God had given me so many chances, and I wasn't showing any appreciation for them. I did some research and decided Steele and I needed to separate for at least 6 months before I could get the divorce proceedings started. When my parents came home, I explained that I needed some time away from Steele. They instantly told me to come back home.

When I told Steele, I was leaving, and he could stay in our home until I got my thoughts together, his only concern was the overhead. "How am I supposed to pay for all this on my own?" To keep the peace, I told him I would still kick in my half of things. He helped me pack and the separation began. They say absence makes the heart grow fonder, and indeed, it's true. He called me every day, left me heartfelt messages, and arranged several "date nights." All of this derailed my plans and I stopped thinking about divorce. We were falling back in love, and I was so thankful God was paving a way for us to survive this.

My paternal grandmother had been sick and succumbed to her illness. This was a devastating blow to my family, but we had all been preparing for it. Steele totally stepped up during that time. He supported and loved on my dad and was even a pallbearer. The day of the funeral, he stayed the night with me at my parents' house. As he wiped my tears and cuddled with me, he said three simple words, "Come home, please." Having him be so vulnerable when I was just as vulnerable was a deadly combination. Two weeks later, I was moving back into our residence and resumed the fight for my marriage.

Although I wasn't sure Steele had changed that much in those short four months, I was hopeful and allowed my faith to lead me. Things were amazing. We literally were thick as thieves and truly enjoyed each other. He made me a priority and I turned my wifely duties up a few notches. We started a number of businesses, worked out together, and truly bonded. Marriage, the way I envisioned it, was happening.

D-Valley

Steele and I hadn't argued in a while and I saw no future storm forming, but all good things come to end, right? One Saturday afternoon, we had a quarrel in the SUV. I had gotten accustomed to being called out of name during arguments, but this day, I'd had enough. My desensitization to being loved correctly was staring me in my face daily. This marriage had become a chore; a task that I no longer felt equipped to complete. I was losing every part of me, and I had a front row seat to my demise.

"Call me a b**** one more time, and I'll kill us both right now n*!gg#." When the rage surfaced, I never knew where it would take me. In the most arrogant and condescending voice possible, Steele quickly glanced at me, and said, "B***, you all talk; you won't do s****." Seat belt came unbuckled and I lunged at the steering wheel. I used one hand to hit him and completely block his view and the other to take control of the wheel trying to crash the SUV. He reacted quickly, screaming and calling me crazy. As he screeched into a nearby parking lot, a full-blown brawl commenced. He kicked and punched, I slapped and bit; we were doing damage. The smoke cleared when we heard a blaring car horn. He was blocking the entrance to the parking lot.

The waterworks followed, from both of us, this time. I had bruises and he had bruises; we couldn't believe we'd almost lost our lives. It was nothing but God watching over us. He glanced at me in disbelief, and said, "We need help! What is happening to us?"

Domestic violence does a number on your mind. I knew what he was capable of and chose to ignore it. There is a level of understanding and forgiveness that eats you alive. While we forgave each other, I wasn't expecting anything to change.

Frustration continued to build, and more disrespect

followed. We had completely lost our way. All the hard work from the previous months, instantly disappeared behind a lack of clarity and lack of ownership. My playbook was empty. I had no other moves to make. We were defeated.

Another physical altercation ensued, this one more dangerous than the last. Aggression and rage created a pure devil in me that evening. Anything that was on hand, I tried to use as a weapon. Extension cords, candy holders, glass coasters, etc. were all flying across our home. The violence escalated to the point where Steele punched me in the face so hard, he detached my retina. My adrenaline was so sky high, that I was unaware until my vision became blurred, and he noticed the blood.

I had to have emergency eye surgery immediately or I would've lost my vision permanently. After enduring the painful, 2-hour, corrective surgery, we were both distraught and exhausted. In a sick twisted way, we stopped to get food on the way back home. We so happened to bump into Ricardo. The hospital required me to wear protective eye shields for at least 6 hours. When Ricardo saw us, his smile turned into a concerned frown. While he kept his composure, he continued to look at me with worry.

The next day at work, I had to face the music. My eye was not healed, but I couldn't afford to take any more time off. My excuse, like most abused women, was "I fell". No one believed me, but they accepted the lie. Ricardo called me into his office and grabbed my bruised face. With tears in his eyes he softly murmured, "Please save yourself Brit." I joked it off and told him he was overreacting. Rosarito came and squeezed me with all her strength, whispering, "You deserve more Brit, I will help you leave." Shame - the shame came back all at once.

Being exposed like that creates a whirlwind of emotions. My life would be taken from me soon, I knew that, yet ignored it because I too could potentially take a life. The lines get blurred when you are victim and abuser. The fact was, no matter how hard Steele and I tried, our spirits could no longer co-exist.

A few weeks later, Steele requested that we separate again. In my heart, I knew this was the correct path to take, but I was blindsided, and it hurt. In my mind I didn't feel he had the right to make that request. My arrogance didn't want to acknowledge his need to save himself, so I refused to separate. In no time, we were back being monsters to each other. I quickly humbled myself and agreed to the separation. We worked opposite schedules, and Steele would never be in our residence at the same time as me. Days would go by, and I would only get "I'm fine" text messages from him.

I had just gotten used to be in our place alone when, he showed up suddenly, one evening. He asked me to leave our home for the duration of our separation until he could "figure things out". "Hell no! I'm not leaving you worthless piece of s@&! When I wanted out, I left, so you leave, stay wherever you been staying."

After that, weeks went by, and I did not hear from him. He also stopped contributing to the household, putting me in severe financial distress. His choice forced me to make a tough decision - let the apartment go and move back in with my parents. The minute I sent him that message, the communication started back up. It was then I had my first intuition about him and another woman. He denied seeing or being with anyone else and pleaded with me to keep our place. It was unfair that I was getting the short end of the stick in, this situation that he had created when I had made it so convenient for him when I had wanted a separation. That was when it really became clear to me that Steele no longer respected me. He didn't care about the fighting. All he wanted was convenience and I was standing in the way.

Difficult times call for difficult decisions. I called Eaglette in a burst of emotions and told her my next plan of action. By the end of the next week, I packed up the entire apartment, excluding Steele's belongings, and headed back to my parents' home. Steele and I had not seen each other. He refused to share any information about his life and only reached out when he needed emergency assistance because he knew I still felt responsible for his well-being. His actions fueled my efforts to get the divorce finalized. The process was excruciating.

The court system makes getting a divorce without a lawyer very difficult. The energy in the "self-help" center is one of shame and blame. Almost as if it's your fault you are making the choice to dissolve the marriage. Instant migraine and hurt is what I felt every time I had to enter that building. In the midst of this, I discovered Steele was, in fact, involved with another woman. He began to flaunt his new love via social media, which I had just reintroduced myself to after years of being off.

Eaglette and I were heading on a "release trip" to Hawaii when I found out. She begged me to not let the news disturb me and focus on the fun we were going to have. While I enjoyed our time together, I cried almost every day of the trip. It was bad timing; my spirit was just too low. Eaglette embraced my emotions every step of the way, she never complained, and never showed any sign of annoyance. We got through the trip, and I made a vow to redirect my focus and change my energy.

Since we were still married, I did my best to maneuver through what I considered blatant disrespect from Steele. His communication with me was inconsistent. He was not aware that I knew about his new love. The new life that he was arrogantly, and proudly, reveling in. To protect my peace, I never mentioned it. He would often contact me for financial assistance, and while I knew better, he was still my husband in my mind and heart, so I would concede.

Those actions alone proved how low I thought of myself and how hopeless I felt about my future. This was not the life I wanted to live; the one I vowed to make happen when I returned from Hawaii. My cup was full. Full of sorrow, confusion, and contradiction. Praying was not something I was comfortable with anymore. My relationship with God was strained and complicated. I did not feel a connection. Unsure of where to guide my frustration, I did my best not to "lash out" at the people around me.

Exploring dating became a thing but I failed miserably. Being broken and attempting to connect with the opposite sex will never be successful. Many of the men instantly saw my weaknesses, identified my desperation, and quickly pounced on the opportunity to take advantage. My ability to still be aware and cautious was a blessing. It was then that I realized God's intentions and plan for me was bigger than my pain

Chapter 7 Genuine Gifted

Rebirth

The battle with the court system continued to be overwhelming. Divorce seemed to be drifting farther and farther away with every flawed document and uneventful court appearance. Steele was still not willing to share his whereabouts, adding more difficulty to the proceedings.

Although my heart was conflicted about him and Heat, I couldn't help but view him as the true love of my life. My extensive and dangerous investigative efforts led me down a rabbit hole of details I was not prepared to handle. Steele wasn't just involved with a woman; he was in love...in love with her and her child. The crushing reality of my infertility was yet again dangling in my face. The father role he had been desperately seeking to fulfill was being honored.

Finally, he agreed to meet and handle the required paperwork. We met at a local Starbucks, and the exchange was stiff, and excruciating, to say the least. He was different, dark, mysterious, and overall unwilling to communicate.

Feeling empty, worthless, and having no reason to feel joy, I sat across from what was once my forever, and watched our contempt for each other play out. We signed all the paperwork, ending the conversation with an awkward "take care".

Scared - I was scared. I was not prepared for this moment. Being a wife was my purpose and I had failed. I just could not accept this failure.

Three weeks after the tense exchange with Steele, I felt a flood of words coming to my heart, but could not articulate them. Keeping a journal was something I had never done before. Even as a little girl, a diary was annoying to me. The concept of writing out your pain was just not conducive to my way of life. However, when I did write, whether for school, work, or in communication with others, the response was always the same. My words on paper would grasp the attention of others quickly.

As I dug deep into this new stage of rebuilding, for some reason, I found myself often wanting to write out the transitions. In my mind, no one would understand a verbal explanation of this pain, except for me, so I didn't think it was worth talking about. Still, I knew I needed to find a way to get it off my chest. So, occasionally, I would open my laptop, and jot down a few random thoughts. In the beginning, it created anger, a constant reminder of the darkness that surrounded me. Reading and being able to reference where I was emotionally, was not therapeutic to me.

It was during this time, LCP Diva, an associate from high

school, randomly reached out to me one evening, requesting we chat about a potential project she wanted me to work on. We had stayed connected through social media, and apparently some of my views and the way they were worded, caught her eye. She had an online publication and wanted me to become a contributor for her. *"Me? Write for someone? No way!"* After a few chats, I began sharing some of my experiences with her and she demanded that I share my testimony as a tool to enlighten and educate other women.

In your darkest hour, God will send you signs of your

purpose. Things will be revealed that you will never

understand. Being obedient during this time is the

difficult part.

Expressing myself in written form was dangerous, and terrifying. It was a daily fight, but LCP Diva was determined to have my voice heard. I started off with a series called "Deactivating", which outlined the beginning stages of my divorce and my overall emotions. In the midst of my fear, I realized that I wanted the little voice I had left to be genuine, real, and soothing. Genuine Gemini was born shortly after.

Genuine Gemini was the woman I once knew. She was bold, she was compassionate, and no nonsense, she also was bruised, but far from broken. The more I curated things for Genuine Gemini, the more I realized everything I was searching for, all the answers I needed truly resided in me. Purpose was forming right before my eyes.

During this transition I met several women who were fighting their own silent battles. It was shocking the number of stories that were similar to mine or worse. Shame was always the common denominator. We all felt the shame of revealing, the shame of forced recanting when not believed, the shame of our tolerance. Quickly, I learned to disarm those willing to share and simply release. My discernment of battered, silenced, women was at an all-time high.

I launched Genuinegemini.com on my 31st birthday, letting go of the shame and never looking back. Genuinegemini.com became a safe haven and truth serum for me and many others. My unfiltered, and optimistic thoughts were plastered weekly in the form of written stories or videos.

In-person events manifested shortly after. Genuine Gemini events were carefully curated to support the voiceless women looking for an outlet, a reason to start over, a reason to believe again. Fear was no longer in the driver's seat. The power of welding women back together and witnessing their impromptu unmasking, is such a priceless gift.

While I worked endlessly to build Genuine Gemini, I noticed a need for validation holding a power as strong as a category 5 hurricane. Social media presented an opportunity to be glorified as an expert without really knowing a thing at all. There was instant gratification when my words, or the graphics associated with them were praised with likes and comments. It gave me the motivation to push forward, however, I quickly learned that not all types of motivation are sustainable. Your "why" will not always get you through, and sometimes, you truly have to fake it until you make it.

I checked statistics daily chasing the feeling of accomplishment like it was heroin. The need to be acknowledged and accepted by the community I was building was taking precedence over the mission...being their voice. Praying became non-existent, once again and my image became the most important thing. The emotions and reflections were afterthoughts until I caught a glimpse of myself in the mirror one evening. My in-home studio was ready for another Genuine Gemini production: perfect lighting, and green screen prepped. I was ready to go but happened to glance at myself prior to hitting record. I didn't recognize myself. *"How did we get back here? How did I work so hard, only to crash and burn again?"*

Outsiders praised my growth, but I knew I had taken several steps back. The vlog was never recorded that day, and future ones were put on hold. That simple glance in the mirror, simple check in, was all I needed to begin the re-evaluation process. Genuine Gemini was not a production, or something worthy of popularity. Genuine Gemini was the back of the house crew, getting everything cleaned and prepped before the show. Genuine Gemini is the coach, running drill after drill with that one player who is full of promise, but lacks courage and a plan of execution. Genuine Gemini is solution giver, and plan implementer. The clout chasing had to die a horrible death. New strategies and a reinvention were on the horiz

Resisting Lonely

Self-awareness had become extremely painful, but completely necessary. After acknowledging a lot of my own flaws, my frustrations and disgust with both Heat and Steele subsided like a rocky wave breaking the beach shore.

I had invested a lot of time meticulously placing blame, but never added my own self-destructive behavior into the equation. The mental battle I fought was, "why were their emotional pain so easily inflicted on me?" I constantly wondered whether or not it was maturity deficiencies or my lack of self-worth. Pressure had formed all around me. Tired of "doing the work," the bubble I had created for myself popped with viscous force and left me no choice but to adjust and maintain.

Genuine Gemini was still evolving, however not in the direction I dreamt. As a woman who survived domestic violence, the embarrassment of my past constantly haunted me. I never intended for my legacy to be associated with beatings and bruises. In my opinion, categorizing myself felt like I accepted and approved of what I'd been through.

There is beauty in healing, there is power in healing, but what we often don't discuss is the confusion and darkness healing brings. Day in and day out you are constantly at war with yourself and others. Your strength becomes questionable, and you patiently sit and wait for the tiny crack in the sky, radiating beautiful sunshine in your dark, toxic bubble.

I waited, but my sunshine was not showing up, at least, not in the way I wanted.

Baffled by the concept of healing, I decided being in pain was easier. There was no confusion there. Self-medicating became a thing. Alcohol and food were the vices. Secretly, I self-sabotaged myself into a whirlpool of repugnance that caused a 60-pound weight gain, and lots of terrible decision making followed.

My body had become my own punching bag. Sad? Cool, go eat. Angry? Great, go have a drink. Feeling envious? Perfect, go eat and drink the evening away. My emotions didn't matter, as long as I could find a way to numb them. Ironically, during this ghastly time, I felt protected and knew I was being prayed for and lifted up as I navigated through this mysterious journey.

During a routine visit to my parents, I caught my mother crying as she stared at an old photo of me. I had to be about 75 pounds lighter back then and had a glow of life that was indescribable. After realizing that I saw her, she quickly hid the picture, and proceeded to greet me.

At that moment, I realized who I was, before this darkness took over, mattered to people, especially my parents. My obligation to myself had died a long heartless death, and I hadn't even realized it. Seeing my mother cry over who I once was, gave me the motivation to at least try... try to be happy...try to be the voice I wanted to be for so many other women. *"But how?!"* How, was always my question.

Back at rock bottom after conquering so much, I felt conflicted with how to resolve the lack of faith. I had a low dose of glory whispering in my ear daily. Church. Church seemed to be the easiest solution to my nagging problem, so I tried becoming more active there, again. During that period, I realized, many people use the church as a pivotal tool for their healing.

Already an extreme introvert, church was a lot for me to handle. It was challenging to face a variety of pure intentions, not knowing who to trust. I didn't believe in the process enough to know how to properly reap the benefits. I needed to see it through however, and continued to push past my discomfort, eventually developing an overall love for all it encompassed. My brand was still important, but I was no longer confident in the mission and understood it was because I lacked self-assurance.

Gaining confidence is not a simple task, in fact, its grueling, and honestly one of the hardest things I've had to do.

Trauma trains us to stay, to remain in dark places

because it's comfortable, its familiar, and effortless.

Being in pain is effortless.

I quickly learned that glory is not given, it is earned. You must work for glory in every aspect of your life. So, this lack of confidence was merely my inability to fight and work for my glory. We all expect that after enduring so much we deserve peace, but, in actuality, we must obtain it.

Instantly, I began to apply immediate pressure towards my glory. Unveiling and unpacking truths that were hidden deep down. Young, Black, and female, therapy seemed good, but I definitely couldn't afford it so getting creative with how I began to repair my brokenness became top priority. Four things I did to get started with that journey was:

- Listened to my pain. Not just allowing the feeling, but dissecting it, until the blows were weakened.

- Held myself accountable for my own toxic emotions and behaviors.

- Positioned myself around people who naturally enhanced me.

- Inspired and mentored at least one person a month; either in my business or personal life.

Giving myself the luxury to fail, I often had to rewrite my playbook, and that always is a remarkable experience. Constantly seeing the challenge ahead and making a choice to "piss or get off the pot," is the most exhilarating thing.

My fight for Glory had just begun, and the only pressure I felt was coming from me.

Chapter 8 Found

The Journey

"Babygirl, it's Mommy. I need to hear your voice. You are

scaring me. Whatever it is, we can fix, but please just let me

know you are ok. Please call me back."

"Brittney, it's Dad. Where are you? You're scaring your mother,

and me too, call me back,

"Sis, come on man, you know I can only handle so much of this.

You gotta come back and help me with these old people; they are

losing their mind. I love you twin! We all we got, please call me

back."

After my careless and insensitive departure, having to face my loved ones brought me severe anxiety, but I knew it had to be done. Make the call, tell them you are okay; relieve their stress.

As heavy as my heart had been, I knew I had more work to do. My purpose was still up for debate, and I knew God wasn't done with me yet. I needed to be found. I needed to be rescued from myself, and no one could do that but me.

My life is valuable, I understood that now. While I might have felt like I was replaceable and disposable to many, I took the time to find the meaning of my own life: I'm a powerhouse Queen and a force to be reckoned with! The legacy I leave behind won't be riddled with pain, agony, and destruction. I refuse!

So, make the call. Let them know you've been FOUND. Found with all your flaws, joy, heart, integrity, and insecurities. Found with more to learn and tons of wisdom to offer. Found with strength and the audacity to fight for better. End this, stop the worry.

So, I made the call. "I'm sorry I worried you. I'm safe and will be home soon."

~

I was startled out of my recurring dream by the persistent ringing of the front desk phone. The dream had finally ended, and I was so thankful to see it through. It was 4p.m. Maldives time. I had landed about 2 hours ago and was severely jet lagged. That didn't stop me from absorbing all this beautiful island had to offer.

I decided to take a nap on the beach. As a solo traveling veteran, you look forward to these moments. The hustle and bustle of travel can be very taxing, and sometimes, the rest is truly what you are seeking.

"Ms. Baker, your suite will be ready shortly, may I offer you a beverage while you wait?" The concierge insisted as I walked towards the piercing blue waters. "Sure, I'll take your best glass of red wine."

The silence was captivating. I quickly positioned myself in one of the cozy cabanas and smiled effortlessly. Purpose looked and felt different in that moment. All the years I had worked to be seen were mirrors I needed to see myself. My heart was full, knowing I had activated a passion for self-worth.

Feeling worthless is like an incurable disease, one that is terminal and seemingly far from a remedy. As a woman, I felt a heavier burden of being perfect and learning to persevere. I let it all go when I traveled. This was country number 19. That number seems so low compared to what's left for me to conquer.

Traveling abroad was my happy place. My special piece of heaven and I adored every minute of it. My eyes began to get heavy as I sipped the last of my wine. I used to be scared to dream, scared to see my future - anticipating it being full of pain. I was liberated from things so many women weren't fortunate enough to escape. My goal was to honor them now.

I made my way to the water and was enamored with the purity of it all. The crashing of the waves was strong, yet contained, and made just enough noise to make you aware of their presence. Eyes closed, I allowed the water to brush my feet and continue to be sun-kissed by God's glory, letting my spirit drift away.

This was no longer a dream. The journey I crafted was perfectly suited for me. *"Was that a win? Absolutely! Did it feel like one? Not all the time."* There was so much more work to discover and do. However, I was up for the challenge.

> Life is humorous when you allow it to be. We all have
> struggles but we must try our best to make it out of
> them. The difference between you and everyone else
> are your efforts, and ability to share, and to enhance.

So, how do you end a journey like mine? Do you close the chapters and never revisit them? Nope, you continue the journey and stay open to the multitude of possibilities...

I'm sure you're wondering, "Well what happened to everyone else?" "What's next?" Life did not stop, and I had to keep showing up. Remembering to be unapologetic about my peace.

Read more about that in Genuine Journey II.

Trust me...you won't be disappointed.

Until then...Be Love!

If you enjoyed this book, please take a moment to write a short review on your favorite online bookstore so others can enjoy it, too.

- Thank you!!

Can't get enough?

Join me every Monday on my podcast Genuinely Gifted - A safe haven... where unlearning and growing and glowing through occurs! There is always a GIFT in the GUTTER. Be Love

Can't Wait For My Next Book?

Join my mailing list brittney@genuinegemini.com get exclusive access to deleted scenes and preview new chapters as I write.

Let's Stay Connected
Instagram: genuinegemini85
Facebook: Brittney Baker

Made in the USA
Coppell, TX
12 July 2021